PAWNEE

THE GREATEST TOWN IN AMERICA

PAWNEE
THE GREATEST TOWN IN AMERICA

Written, Compiled, Researched, Typed, Collated, Proofread, and Run Through Spell Check

by

LESLIE KNOPE

Deputy Director, Department of Parks and Recreation

With Nate DiMeo and the Creative Team of *Parks and Recreation*

HYPERION
NEW YORK

ⓗⓨⓟⓔⓡⓘⓞⓝ

NBCUniversal
Television Consumer Products

Parks and Recreation is a trademark and copyright of Universal Network Television, LLC.
All Rights reserved.

Copyright ©2011 Universal City Studios Productions, LLLP. All Rights Reserved.

Library of Congress Cataloging-in-Publication Data

Pawnee : the greatest town in America / written, compiled, researched, typed,
collated, proofread, and run through spell check by Leslie Knope. — 1st ed.
    p. cm.
  Fictitiously attributed to Leslie Knope, a character on the NBC television show, Parks
and recreation, that is set in the fictional Indiana town, Pawnee.
    ISBN 978-1-4013-1064-6
  1. Parks and recreation (Television program) I. Hyperion (Publisher)
    PN1992.77.P2655P39 2011
    791.45—dc22

                                                        2011015148

Hyperion books are available for special promotions and premiums. For details
contact the HarperCollins Special Markets Department in the New York office
at 212-207-7528, fax 212-207-7222, or email spsales@harpercollins.com.

Designed by: Timothy Shaner, nightanddaydesign.biz

FIRST EDITION

10 9 8 7 6 5 4 3 2 1

Dedication

To the good people of Pawnee. And to the people who have worked hard to make this town great. And to everyone, anywhere, who loves his/her hometown, or his/her adopted hometown, and to every person who understands the importance of citizenship. And to the founding fathers (and mothers) of this great country, and to everyone who has fought, in any way, to keep this country free and safe, and to the framers of the Constitution, and to everyone in the entire world, and to the makers of BrainBlast™ XXX-Treme N-R-G Drink, which has done a bang-up job of getting me through these last fifty-five hours of working on this book with no sleep. Okay. That's enough.

I just tried to go to sleep, and that's a non-starter, with the (by my count) 256-plus ounces of BrainBlast™ XXX-Treme N-R-G Drink coursing through my veins. It honestly feels like my eyeballs are spinning around in my head like tiny basketballs on a Globetrotter's finger. So here's some more: this is dedicated to my family, and my friends, and the good people of Pawnee, and Spider-Man, and every living creature in the universe except turtles, whom I find condescending, and to whatever mad genius scientist came up with BrainBlast™ XXX-Treme N-R-G drink, because, *damn*, and to the good people of Pawnee, and most of all, to Pawnee, the Greatest Town in America, and by that I mean to the actual town, not the book *Pawnee: The Greatest Town in America*, I'm not dedicating this book to itself. I mean, I feel really weird right now but I'm not that weird.

And finally, to the good people of Pawnee. I should probably read this over once just to make sure it's good, but I currently have what I would describe as "double-reverse tunnel vision" and it's hard to focus, so I'm just going to assume it's fine.

Contents

Acknowledgments

The Author would like to thank her coworkers at City Hall and the Department of Parks and Recreation: Ann Perkins, Tom Haverford, April Ludgate, Andy Dwyer, Donna Meagle, Chris Traeger, and Ben Wyatt. And The Author's boss, Ron Swanson, who is dead wrong about literally everything involving the role of government in people's lives but is also, secretly, the kindest and most decent man The Author has ever met.

Jerry Gergich also helped The Author, but his massive printing screwup kind of undid a lot of the positive stuff he contributed to The Author, and frankly, even though The Author likes Mr. Gergich a lot, The Author is still pretty steamed at him. When Mr. Gergich showed The Author that he had printed the cover upside down, causing The Author to have to spend the entire night before the publication date at a Kinko's pounding BrainBlast™ XXX-Treme N-R-G drinks and chocolate-covered espresso beans just to stay awake, it basically took everything in The Author's power not to drive over to Mr. Gergich's house at five in the morning and pound on the door and scream at Mr. Gergich and ask Mrs. Gergich how she could stand living with Mr. Gergich for thirty years without stuffing a toaster down his throat while he sleeps. But then she calmed down and now everything is fine.

The historical portions of this book were largely written from memory by The Author, then fact-checked by both Bill Haggerty of the Pawnee Historical Society and a team of researchers from Pawnee Community College, who proclaimed them to be "shockingly accurate." There's really no reason for The Author to include that fact here, except that The Author is feeling a little braggy and she wants everyone to know that she basically typed this from memory.

Leslie Knope
October 2011

Author's Note

The Author was really excited to refer to herself as "The Author" throughout this book, because it just seemed so official and kickass and cool, but now, when The Author has read back over the Acknowledgments on the previous pages, it seems stilted and weird. So from now on, I'll just call myself Leslie. I hope everyone is cool with that.

I really want you to love this book!

Love,
Leslie Knope
October 2011

*There is nothing wrong with America that cannot
be cured by what is right with America.*

—BILL CLINTON, U.S. PRESIDENT (1992–2000)

*It's passionately interesting for me that the things that I
learned in a small town, in a very modest home, are just
the things that I believe have won the election.*

—MARGARET THATCHER, BRITISH PRIME MINISTER (1979–1990)

*It's not necessary to go far and wide. I mean, you can really
find exciting and inspiring things within your hometown.*

—DARYL HANNAH, SHE WAS IN *SPLASH*

PAWNEE

THE GREATEST TOWN IN AMERICA

Introduction

Let me take you on a journey.

Get in your car and drive south on beautiful Route 37, marveling at the natural beauty that surrounds you in the very heart of America's Heartland. Situated in the rolling hills of southern Indiana, resting on the intersection of the Norman Uplands and the Mitchell Plain, lies a city dotted with pumpkin ash and white cedar trees. The abundant limestone creates a beautiful landscape of sinks, ravines, fissures, underground streams, springs, and caves. You are in a city that teems with promise, that revels in its history, and which houses thousands of our nation's best and brightest as they strive for degrees in all areas of higher education.

This is Bloomington. About thirty-five miles past that is Pawnee.

Here in Pawnee, the white cedar trees don't sway as beautifully, as many of them were removed to make room for a series of now-abandoned cement-mixing plants. We do not have the stunning Indiana University campus, but we do have the practical Pawnee Institute for Corn Syrup Research and Camera Repair. And no, the famous Indiana limestone foundation did not grace us with many springs or caves, but we do have fissures. Lots and lots of fissures. Most structures in town have been, at some point, basically swallowed by a fissure. Sometimes just driving to the grocery store is a crazy not-worth-it gamble in terms of tire blowouts. One time in the 1940s a two-star general drove through Pawnee and thought that we had been bombed by the Germans somehow and called President Roosevelt and like twenty battleships went on ready-alert 1. There are a lot of fissures, is what I'm saying.

No, we're not Indianapolis. And maybe we're not even Bloomington. But what Pawnee

1

lacks in fame or beauty, we make up for in heart. Like the pudgy, sarcastic best friend in a romantic comedy, we are actually really interesting and cool if you look hard enough.

This is a community of friendly, hardworking people, who know the value of a dollar, the power of a smile, and thanks to the local corn syrup factory, the warning signs of early-onset diabetes. Everyone in this town can tell you a story of a neighbor helping them in a time of need, with everything from changing a friend's fissure-created flat tire to emergency late-night bedroom animal removal. (See "History of the Pawnee Raccoon Problem," Chapter 4.)

Pawnee has had its ups and downs, its highs and lows. We've had both wonderful heroes and miserable villains. We've had triumphs, and we've had plenty of failures. Our history is the history of America itself, and if you choose to come spend some time with us, you will leave a changed person. So drive on down Route 37 and see what we have to offer. Don't stay in Bloomington. They're a bunch of snobs. "Oh, our limestone caves are so pretty, our campus is so great." Get over yourselves, Bloomington.

This book is your guide to everything we have to offer: a comprehensive look at our past, present, and future—warts and all. Every page has a wonderful Pawnee story to tell, so read the book straight through, or flip through it at random. Just don't leave it in your bathroom. I worked really hard on this, and it would bum me out to think of it just sitting on the gross floors of people's bathrooms.

In short: Welcome to Pawnee. We hope you stay awhile.

Leslie Knope
October 2011

Pawnee at a Glance

Incorporated: 1817

De-Incorporated due to Famine, Corruption, and a Host of Other Problems: 1818

Re-Incorporated, This Time for Good: 1819

Population (a/o 2010 census): 66,218, plus or minus ~5,000[1]

Mayor: Walter Gunderson (1994–present)

Median Household Income: $38,360

Highest Point: Larry Joe Bird Municipal Landfill (263 ft)[2]

---

[1] There were some problems with our local census form collector. He turned out not to be super reliable, and traded some of the census forms to this weird Russian guy for cold medicine.

[2] Larry Bird, AKA "The Hick from French Lick," is not from Pawnee. But he did once drive through here, legend has it, looking for tools to re-pave his mom's driveway, and that's more than enough to get like fifteen different things in town named after him.

Lowest Point: Devil's Fissure (unknown)[3]

Denonym: Pawneean

Sister Cities: Sarajevo, Bosnia-Herzegovina; Krakow, Poland; Pyongyang, North Korea; Kinshasa, Democratic Republic of Congo; Boraqua, Venezuela

Official City Tree: Indiana Common Shrub[4]

Official City Bird: Giant Grizzled-Neck Cackling Pigeon[5]

Official City Drink: Frooties!™ Carbonated Corn Syrup

Largest Bodies of Water:

1. Pawnee River

2. Indian Tears Pond

3. Sweetums Plant Toxic Outflow Repository 7D

Largest Employers:

1. Sweetums Confectionary Corp.

2. City of Pawnee

3. Pawnee St. Joseph's Medical Center

4. Various fast-food restaurants owned by Yum! Brands of Louisville, KY

5. Kernston's Rubber Nipples

6. Norton Construction

7. (tie) The Glitter Factory (gentlemen's club)

7. (tie) The Glitter Factory (glitter manufacturer and children's party supplier)

9. Halverson, Bundle, Korbitz, Lasceaux, Pfeffingham, Wingback, and Spinkt, P.C.[6]

10. Don's Cement

---

[3] I asked the U.S. Geological Survey to assist us in finally determining just how deep Devil's Fissure is. Despite my clever use of the phrase "get to the bottom of it," they refused, checking off the boxes marked "Budget Constraints" and "Gross Indifference." In lieu of a federal survey, I will quote official town documents, which alternately list its depth as "Approximately 150 feet below sea level" and "Red China."

[4] The Indiana Common is a pretty ugly shrub, even for a shrub—short, prickly, brown, and gross. But attempts by some local advocates to get our Official City Tree changed to something more noble—like the beech or poplar or the Whomping Willow from *Harry Potter* or really freaking *anything* but the Indiana Common Shrub—have fallen on deaf ears, for reasons that frankly escape those same local advocates.

[5] Don't even get the local advocates started on those damned pigeons. Just because they're *everywhere* doesn't mean we have to give them an award.

[6] Famous in town for their nearly constant TV ad jingle: "If you're in the clink / Call Halverson, Bundle, Korbitz, Lasceaux, Pfeffingham, Wingback, and Spinkt!" The crummy slant rhyme notwithstanding, that sucker will stay in your head for months.

SuperFUNd[7] sites:

Krendell Canal

Sweetums Plant Toxic Outflow Repositories 2G and 7F

Local Hospital: The AMA Award–Winning Pawnee St. Joseph's Medical Center[8]

Demographics: Pawnee is proud of its diverse racial makeup:

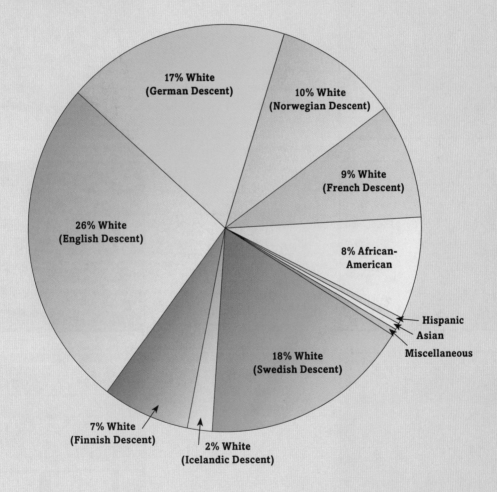

[7] A 2002 initiative from the Southern Indiana Bureau of Tourism and Development called for the rebranding of the city's two federal Super Fund toxic cleanup sites. The winning new name was SuperFUN!d—the exclamation point eventually got removed because it looked like a typo. The same initiative also required that environmental reports that referred to "fecal contaminants" include an official notation that "God made dirt and dirt don't hurt."

[8] Pawnee St. Joe's was named by the AMA as one of the Top 10 Indiana Medical Facilities for both "Covered Parking" and "Halloween Decorations."

TOWN SLOGANS THROUGH THE YEARS

1820–1824
"Pawnee: The Paris of America!"

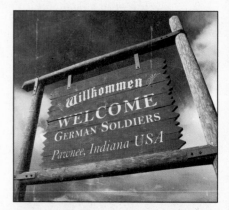

1824–1880
"Pawnee: The Akron of Southwest Indiana"

1880–1939
"Pawnee: A Town and a Place"

1939–1945
"Pawnee: "Welcome, German Soldiers"[9]

1945–1964
"Pawnee: The Factory Fire Capital of America"

1964–1974
"Pawnee: Welcome, Vietnamese Soldiers!"

[9] After the Nazis took France, our mayor kind of panicked.

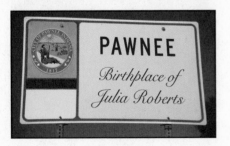

1974–1976
"Pawnee: Engage with Zorp"[10]

1976
"Pawnee: Zorp Is Dead. Long Live Zorp"

1977–1985
"Pawnee: It's Safe to Be Here Now!"

1985–1988
"Pawnee: Birthplace of Julia Roberts"[11]

1988–2001
"Pawnee: Home of the World Famous Julia Roberts Lawsuit"

2001–2009
"Pawnee: Welcome, Taliban Soldiers!"

2009–Present
"Pawnee: First in Friendship, Fourth in Obesity"

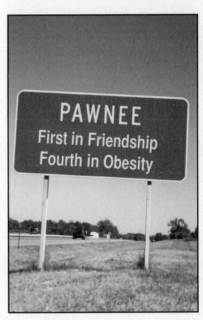

[10] For two years, Pawnee was overtaken by a cult. See Chapter 4, "Interview with a Reasonableist."

[11] This was a lie. She sued, and we had to change it.

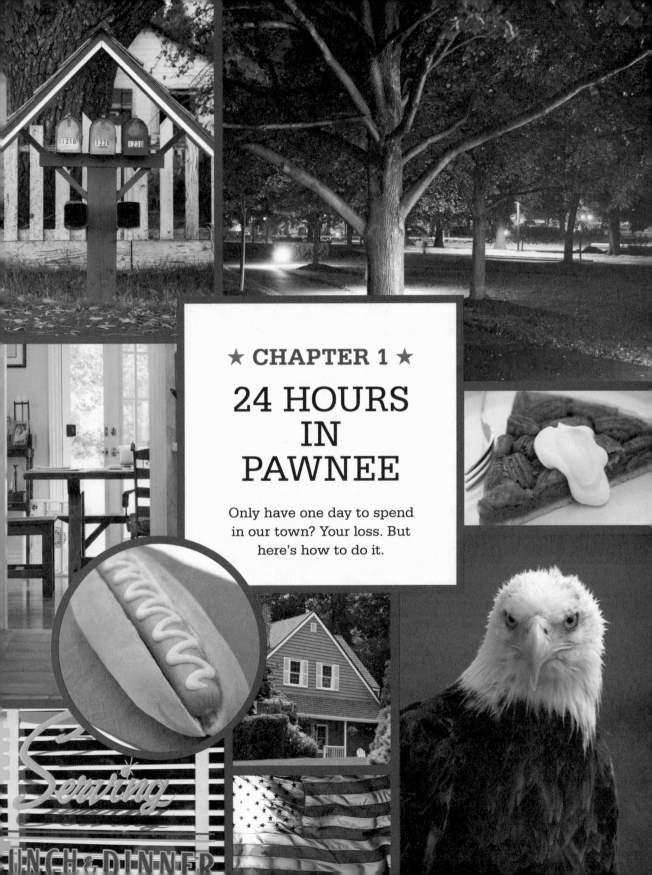

★ CHAPTER 1 ★

24 HOURS IN PAWNEE

Only have one day to spend in our town? Your loss. But here's how to do it.

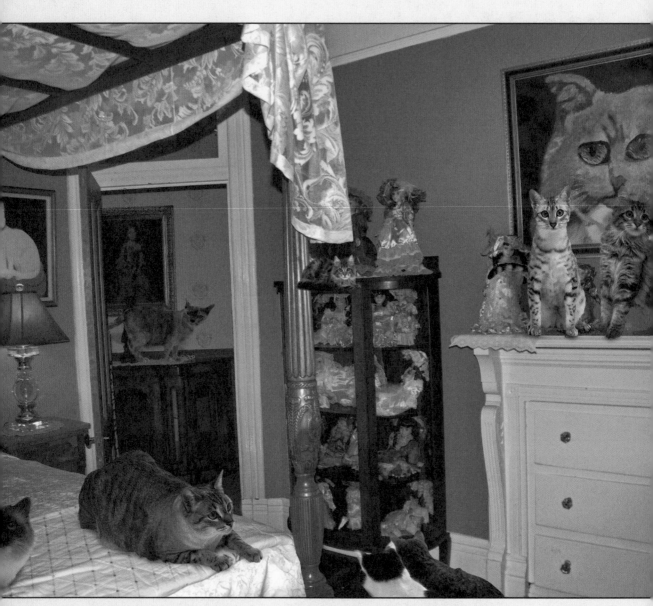

These are just a few of the unreasonably high number of cats living in The Quiet Corn.

1

I am *very* excited for you.

I was born here in this amazing town, so I do not remember what it was like to experience it for the first time. Thank you for the opportunity to let me try to imagine it. You have so much ahead of you. My god, the possibilities. My *god*.

You really need a minimum of four to thirty weeks to see everything there is to see, but if you only have a short time, what follows is the perfect one-day "must-see" tour of Pawnee. Off you go!

5:30 A.M.

GOOD MORNING! How does it feel to wake up in the **best city in America**? To get the blood flowing, let's do some **jumping jacks** in your hotel room. Now some **sit-ups**. Now you're ready. Wait: do some **lunges**, and sing your favorite song out loud—I find that really puts you in a great mood. My favorite song is **"Running Down a Dream"** by Tom Petty. Sing it really loudly, and air-guitar the guitar parts. Did you sing it? Okay, *now* you're ready.

If you're the type who appreciates an authentic, down-home feel, you're probably staying in **The Quiet Corn Bed and Breakfast** (17 Percy Street). Innkeeper Delores Clack will ensure that you

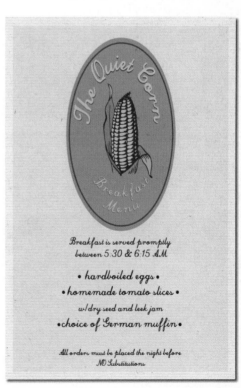

The Quiet Corn
Breakfast Menu

Breakfast is served promptly
between 5:30 & 6:15 A.M.

• hardboiled eggs •
• homemade tomato slices •
w/ dry seed and leek jam
• choice of German muffin •

All orders must be placed the night before
NO Substitutions

experience exactly what life was like in Pawnee at the turn of the century, right down to the charming old furniture, unreliable plumbing, and positively unbending rule against even moderate noise after seven P.M.

Every Tuesday, Delores leads a **walking tour of Pawnee's most interesting mailboxes**. She moves very slowly, however, so only take this tour if all you are interested in seeing, for the entire day, is four moderately interesting mailboxes.

If you're allergic to cats, or even just don't like them, or like them but don't like thirty-plus of them milling around you at a time, or if you have even a slight aversion to airborne mold spores, The Quiet Corn is not for you. So you may have chosen one of our many excellent mo- and hotels. The **Pawnee SuperSuites** (380 Drexel Avenue) provides reasonably priced accommodations with free broadcast television and beautiful views of Drexel Avenue. Most of their doors can be successfully locked for privacy, and while the cleaning staff may not be "friendly," they almost always do their appointed job. Except for **Clara**. If Clara is assigned to your room you are basically screwed.

In a pinch, the downtown **Four Seasoms Pawnee** (320 Tellenson Avenue) will

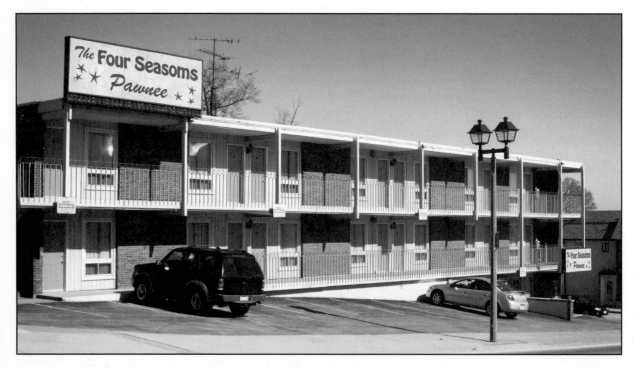

The Four Seasoms Pawnee. It's not great, but it's better than the Pawnee Rytz Karltonne.

do. (Please note the spelling—it's "Seasoms," not "Seasons." A small but critical difference.)

If you are really lucky, you may just be waking up in a **private home**, due to one of our uncommonly generous locals, who has demonstrated the legendary "Pawnee Hospitality" that is known far and wide and invited you to stay over!

Note: do not stay with the man pictured at the right. His name is **Gary Murdeen**, and he is not hospitable. He is tricky, and he likes to invite people to rent his guest room and then draw pictures on their butts while they sleep.

Gary is not hospitable.

6:00 A.M.

HEAD INTO THE SHOWER. Use a shower cap if you don't want to get your hair wet. (Some of this stuff I may not have to tell you, but I really want this day to be perfect, so I'm leaving nothing to chance.)

6:30 A.M.

THROW ON YOUR SMARTEST BLAZER and comfortablest walking shoes and make a beeline for Pawnee's breakfast landmark (and my personal round-the-clock restaurant of choice) **JJ's Diner**! (122 Sunderland, between TrampStamp Tattoos and the ChloroTech Cadmium Refinery). Pawnee's premier waffle location opened in 1976, forever changing the lives of me and everyone else who likes things that are amazing. Grab the best seat in the house before Kyle snags it—the **corner booth near the rotating pie display**. Gaze out at the hustle and bustle of Sunrise in Pawnee and sip on the **morning brew**, being careful not to spill anything, because I swear to God I love the place, but it's like pulling teeth to get **extra napkins**. You would think you had asked for a **bald eagle feather** or something. If you get **Kevin** as a waiter, pretend you forgot something in your car and come back and take a different table.

The **waffles** are the signature dish of JJ's, and no trip to Pawnee is complete without them. Get the double stack, and order more when you're about halfway done. Parks

Former Vice President **Dan Quayle** once sat in this booth. Only for coffee— he turned down the waffles because he said he "wasn't hungry." No one ever said the guy was a genius.

This rotating pie display is referred to by locals as **"The Widow-Maker"** because the pies are so sweet they will kill you, or make you so fat that your wife will leave you. Both things have actually happened.

These five booths are informally reserved for **old, angry people**.

This booth, near the heating vent, is great in the winter. In summer, avoid it at all costs, because the heat cannot be turned off. From June to like September, this booth is a **horrifying collage** of **molten vinyl** with **strips of human skin that have sort of melted into it like cheese** and **white-hot, expired ketchup bottles** that smell like **death**.

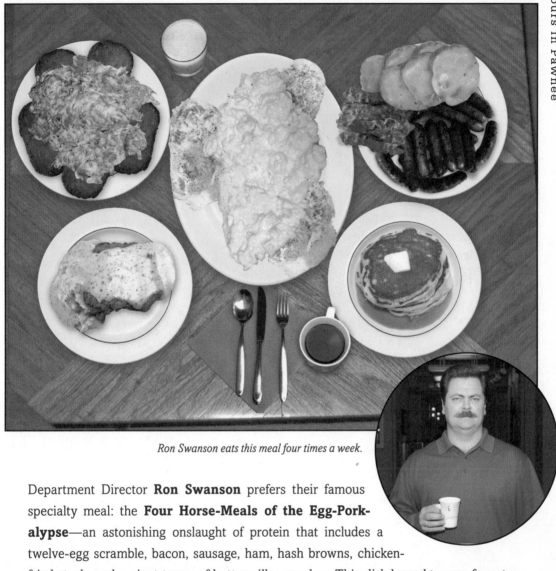

Ron Swanson eats this meal four times a week.

Department Director **Ron Swanson** prefers their famous specialty meal: the **Four Horse-Meals of the Egg-Pork-alypse**—an astonishing onslaught of protein that includes a twelve-egg scramble, bacon, sausage, ham, hash browns, chicken-fried steak, and a giant tower of buttermilk pancakes. This dish brought some fame to Pawnee in May of 1998, when it was officially "condemned" by both the American Heart Association and Doctors Without Borders.

If you're lucky, you may be able to speak with owner **J.J. Lipscomb** himself, but whatever you do, don't bring up his ex-wife **Donna**—who, due to J.J.'s many indiscretions, and their subsequent acrimonious divorce, will be receiving 90 percent of your waffle money—unless you like forceful and creative cursing.

Knope Tip: I like to order **waffle toppings as coffee toppings**. Tell your server you want the "Leslie Knope," and enjoy a large coffee with whipped cream and syrup. Trust me, it is delicious.

Here's a photo collage of me eating waffles over the years:

"Battle of Indian Hill," by Ian Phillips, 1982. The local cavalrymen were not super smart.

9:30 A.M.

TIME TO TAKE IN SOME OF PAWNEE'S HISTORY. First, stop by the site of the **Battle of Indian Hill** (information kiosk at 100 Wacote Avenue). On this site in 1884, an epic seven-day battle was fought between the Pawnee cavalry division and the Wamapoke natives, who eventually lost because they did not have any weapons. **Chief Wakote**, who was ninety-three years old, showed uncommon valor by repeatedly repelling the advancing and heavily armed Pawneeans with nothing more than rocks, sticks, and mind games. At one point, staring right down the barrel of several cavalry shotguns, he pointed behind them and said, **"Hey—look over there!"** and fled to safety as the (let's face it) moronic soldiers searched the horizon behind them in vain for something interesting. This is thought by historians to be the first ever use of "Hey, look over there."

Eventually, Chief Wakote was shot 102 times by the cavalry, and his loyal followers were routed—another sad chapter in America's cruel and shameful history with Native Americans. Pick up a **rainstick** at the **gift shop**!

11:30 A.M.

A SWEET TOOTH'S PARADISE. Recapture your childhood sense of wonder when you step through the doors of the famous **Sweetums** Factory (1 Sweetums Way), Pawnee's answer to Willy Wonka's Chocolate Factory, minus the orange dwarves and child abuse. Much more on Sweetums later, but for now, take the forty-five-minute tour and see why Pawnee is called "A Sweet Tooth's Paradise." Also, learn why it is the fourth most obese city in America.

12:30 P.M.

SITE OF THE PAWNEE BREAD FACTORY FIRE. Head on over to the corner of Howland and Baker Streets, in Pawnee's historic Factory District. Now close your eyes. What's that you hear? Is it the sound of screaming, non-union workers fleeing for their lives? And what do you smell? Burning bread, perhaps? You're not having a stroke.[12] You're reliving history.

This is the site of the old **Pawnee Bread Factory**, which at one time employed more than three thousand Pawneeans, before it burned down in 1922. The site (now host to a Taco Bell/KFC, a locksmith, and a Papa John's/Taco Bell Express) is commemorated by a small plaque, which could really use some polishing, dammit, I have to remember to do that, but which, if you look close enough, tells the story of one of the greatest disasters in Pawnee history.

But also one of the most heroic, as a man named **William Percy** rushed into the burning building and rescued the beloved secret recipe for Pawnee Pumpernickel! Sadly, more than thirty people perished in the flames, though I'd like to think that they died happily, watching Percy rush out of the building, secret recipe intact. Percy was later elected mayor for his heroism, despite the eventual realization that the recipe had been published in a cookbook a year earlier.

---

[12] I hope. If you are, get to Pawnee St. Joe's Hospital immediately. Ask for "Ann."

Don't Bother: PAWNEE LIBRARY

Do you enjoy the feeling of having a billion tiny shards of glass rubbed into your eyeballs by a diseased ape? If so, head on down to the festering bowels of the **Pawnee Public Library**. The main branch was built in 1904 and is still standing, despite being rendered irrelevant by computers and technology. If you do head over, beware, because according to some respected medical people I have spoken to but can't name here for complicated reasons, more than 80 percent of all diseases are spread through the filthy pages of library books.

The **main reading room** is awash in sickening, blindingly bright light, and features a bunch of **terrible human beings** staring at you like you're a **shoplifter** while you try to peruse a book in their **putrid repository**. Suffer **snotty looks** and **condescending gestures** from **idiotic women** who really and truly believe they are smarter and better than you are but in reality have **rat-level IQs**. Just stay away. It's the worst place in the world. I hate it so much—they are **evil**, evil people. Imagine this: someone fabricates a book, gives it a ridiculous title (***Whoa Is Me: How I Finally Had My First Orgasm at Age 35***), then falsifies documents to make it look like you checked it out of the library a year ago, then bills you for the overdue charges, and when you refuse to pay, "leaks" the story to the *Pawnee Journal*. Can you wrap your head around that **disgusting pettiness**? That **corruption**?

Parents, keep your children away from this **fetid hellhole** and don't let them look directly into the eyes of the **demon-brained succubuses** behind the checkout desk.

The **Howell Street Branch** is actually kind of nice.

This place sucks eggs.

1:30 P.M

LUNCH. Hungry? I bet you are, after your busy morning. Pawnee has dozens of excellent restaurants, and quite literally hundreds of convenient fast-food outlets, kiosks, carts, and bulk-rate warehouses. But I'm seriously going to recommend you just go back to **JJ's Diner**, because honestly, what do they put in those waffles? Cocaine?

If you're looking for some great 'za, we've got it, at **Three Jacks Pizza** (39 Lowell Street, just past Roger's Big 'N' Tall Irregular Men's Swimsuits). Feeling especially peckish? **Big Head Joe's** (140 Memorial Boulevard, just steps from City Hall) is the home of the **Meat Tornado Burrito**. Weighing in at an unnecessary nine pounds, the Meat Tornado is available as of this writing, pending a lawsuit resulting from the death of a fifty-eight-year-old man with an irregular heartbeat who was dared to stick the entire thing in his mouth. If you're looking for more exotic fare, hit **Bistro Desmarches** (338 Hensley Street), which has the distinction of being the first restaurant in our town's history to have a French-sounding name. (The food is just normal turkey sandwiches and stuff.)

3–5:00 P.M.

WALK IT OFF! After all those delicious waffles (you went back to JJ's, right? I hope so) you can walk off the calories by going on a leisurely stroll. Put away your iPods and/or CD Walkmen and take in the sights and sounds of Pawnee. Listen for the distinctive call of our state bird, the **cardinal**. Gaze at the beautiful blooms on our state tree, the **yellow poplar**. Luxuriate in the soothing white noise of **traffic.**

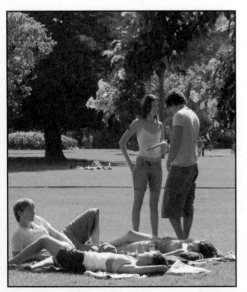

If parks are your thing, well, you're in luck. Pawnee has several that are perfect for leisurely strolls, people-watching, and fun-enjoying. (It also has some that should generally be avoided. More on this later.) The prettiest is **Harvey James Park** (intersection of Calbert and Naughton Streets), a beautiful open-area play space teeming with children, dogs, and merriment. One word of caution: in winter, the northern half tends to be **raccoon-**

Beautiful Harvey James Park. Stick to the southern end to avoid a potentially rabid surprise.

controlled. Stick to the southern half, and if you hear a terrifying crescendo of clicks, chirps, and buzzes, lift small children off the ground and hustle your way out of there.

After the stroll, circle back to **JJ's Diner** for a late-afternoon coffee and syrup pick-me-up, then head over to the **Hompherman Snow Globe Museum** (just two blocks down Sunderland on the right), which features more than fifteen hundred beautiful pieces. Warning: *Do not shake the snow globes*. They are for display only, and the proprietors will get very mad at you. I know, it's confusing.

5:00 P.M.

BATHROOM BREAK. I don't know if you really need me to include this, but as I've been typing up your schedule I got worried that you maybe haven't gone, so I thought I'd put this in now just in case.

5:30 P.M.

"OUR GREATEST HOME." Stately **Turnbill Mansion** (built 1860) was described by Mayor Percy as "Pawnee's greatest private home," during his eulogy for owner Reverend

TURNBILL MANSION
MR. TURNBILL'S DEN (SMOKING PARLOUR)

LEFT: *The Reverend Turnbill himself. The chair upon which he is seated was carved by his gardener's 5 year old son (before the child labor laws were enforced.*
BELOW: *The Smoking Room before the fire.*

BELOW:
Reverend Turnbill's smoking pipe, imported all the way from Eagleton, Indiana.

Reverend Turnbill was a man of few needs: Christ, gin, and fine tobacco. The den was his sanctuary, a place to escape the pressures of his family and church congregation where he could meditate and inebriate. After his sermon, he'd have his servin'. That is, until a small fire which set the room ablaze.

This stately manor house will transport you back in time to an era when people did not know how to fully secure chandeliers to their ceilings.

Jeremiah Turnbill, who died when the house was mostly destroyed by a tornado in 1898. It has since been completely restored, and the half-hourly tours transport you back to a bygone era of grace, elegance, and creaky floors. Make sure you take a picture of the **Grand Room** and its magnificent **chandelier**, which may remind you of the one in *Phantom of the Opera*, right down to the fact that this one periodically comes crashing down to the floor unexpectedly.

7:30 P.M.

DINNER. You know where you should go. They serve breakfast 24/7. And you know you've been thinking about those waffles.

If you want dinner food, my favorite haunt is **Al Dente** fine Italian dining (830 Roscoe St., across from the Taco Bell/Pizza Hut/Dunkin' Donuts). Chef Carl Milweed will delight your taste buds with a wide assortment of cheese-covered pastas, meat-and-cheese dishes, and fried cheeses. (For other, more exotic restaurant choices, see Chapter 2 for a list of Pawnee's Best Ethnic Restaurants.)

9:30 P.M.

PAINT THE TOWN RED. If you're not exhausted yet, there is plenty to do after dark! In the summertime, **Harvey James Park** hosts **movie night** on the Great Lawn, showing classic black-and-white screwball comedies from the golden era of Hollywood. No one ever goes. It's sad. But you should go!

If you're looking for a little more spice, Pawnee does have its share of bars, dance halls, and Gentleman's Clubs, but in the interest of propriety, I will not officially recommend any of them in particular. (Just stay away from the **Glitter Factory**. Or, as many Pawnee doctors call it, "Hepatitis Alley.")

11:30 P.M.

BEDTIME. Sleep well! *Friends* is on Channel 9 here. And then at midnight they show another *Friends* on Channel 11.

Oh no—your day is over! There is so much more you could've done. Frankly, I'm a little disappointed in you. You didn't even get to tour **Kernston's Rubber Nipple Factory**. You never paid homage at the **Li'l Sebastian Memorial** at the Pawnee Zoo, or tried your luck at the **Wamapoke Casino**, or went to the **Rock and Roll Bowling Lanes**. Oh well—looks like you'll just have to stay a little longer. I'll call the car rental place and tell them you need to extend your contract. You call whoever you need to call on your end.

And I'll see you tomorrow morning at 6:30 at JJ's!

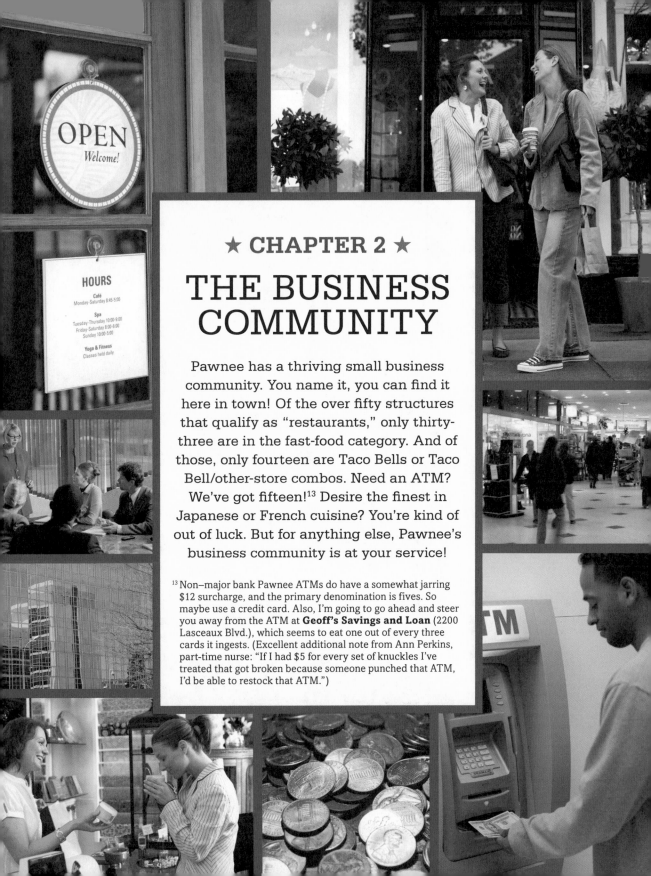

★ CHAPTER 2 ★

THE BUSINESS COMMUNITY

Pawnee has a thriving small business community. You name it, you can find it here in town! Of the over fifty structures that qualify as "restaurants," only thirty-three are in the fast-food category. And of those, only fourteen are Taco Bells or Taco Bell/other-store combos. Need an ATM? We've got fifteen![13] Desire the finest in Japanese or French cuisine? You're kind of out of luck. But for anything else, Pawnee's business community is at your service!

[13] Non–major bank Pawnee ATMs do have a somewhat jarring $12 surcharge, and the primary denomination is fives. So maybe use a credit card. Also, I'm going to go ahead and steer you away from the ATM at **Geoff's Savings and Loan** (2200 Lasceaux Blvd.), which seems to eat one out of every three cards it ingests. (Excellent additional note from Ann Perkins, part-time nurse: "If I had $5 for every set of knuckles I've treated that got broken because someone punched that ATM, I'd be able to restock that ATM.")

2

Sweetums: A Pawnee Institution

John Chester Newport had a dream. Shot in the leg while running away from the Battle of Spotsylvania Court House, the nineteen-year-old private lay in a Union field hospital in May of 1864. As the doctor's morphine hit his bloodstream, and as his leg was removed below the knee with a rusty saw, Newport dreamt of home. He saw the rolling fields of Pawnee . . . the setting sun reflected in the crystal clear waters of Indian Tears Pond . . . and he saw a giant blue owl smoking a long pipe, and then he saw the owl's face change into the face of his mother, except she was way younger and had a flute for an arm, and somehow he knew that her best friend was a beaver who lived in a magic bag and wore a jacket made of gravy. And when he finally woke up from that fever dream, he had an epiphany: he really, really loved morphine.

Upon returning to Pawnee and starting a moderately successful business letting children touch his stump, Newport began whipping up batches of sweet treats that soon had his neighbors hooked. Because they were loaded with opiates. People found they needed to buy more and more to achieve the same level of deliciousness, and before long, Sweetums Corp. was the most successful business in town.

LEFT: Built on the vision of one great dreamer and the addictive qualities of Schedule-1 narcotics, the Sweetums Corporation has long been Pawnee's most high-profile business. RIGHT: If it weren't for John Newport's crippling addiction to morphine, Pawnee kids wouldn't have such amazing Halloweens!

27

Sweetums ad, 1880, designed by John Newport himself, while zonked on morphine.

In addition to finding his calling as a candy maker, Newport also found he had a way with advertising. This nineteenth-century Don Draper[14] coined one of the first successful slogans in American Corporate history: "No One Can Eat Just One—Because They Have Drugs in Them."[15] As the company grew, the Sweetums food scientists slavishly followed Newport's mantra: "Can we get more morphine in there?" And for years afterward, Sweetums' slogan remained "Morphine is Job One."[16]

After Newport died of a morphine overdose, his son John Newport, Jr., took over the company. In 1894, he proudly decreed that Sweetums products "would no longer contain morphine, but would instead be fortified with the healthfull-est of health ingredients, such as birch bark, peppermint oil, and cocaine." Sweetums' most popular confections at the time were bite-sized chocolate snacks called Jitters, named after the prolonged fits of giddy shaking their delighted consumers would experience after eating them.

[14] CableTastic!, Pawnee's primary cable provider, does not carry AMC, but I have heard Tom talk about *Mad Men* and think it sounds a little hoity-toity.

[15] Years later, Lay's potato chips would coincidentally use the first half of this slogan, leading many in Pawnee to suspect (baselessly) that Lay's were laced with narcotics.

[16] Years later, Ford Motor Company would coincidentally use the slogan,"Quality is Job One," leading many in Pawnee to suspect (again, baselessly) that Ford vehicles were somehow addictive.

From 1912 to 1914, all of Sweetums' products contained massive amounts of black-tar heroin.

After John Newport, Jr., died of a cocaine overdose, the company fell into the hands of his brother Albix Newport. During World War I, Albix contributed large quantities of money to war bonds. Controversially, they were war bonds to support the German Empire. This began after a famous meeting between American business leaders and Kaiser Wilhelm II in Vienna in 1913. "I looked the man in the eye," said Albix, "and I found him to be very straightforward and trustworthy. I was able to get a sense of his soul. Also, he promised me that when the war ended I could have Denmark."[17] After the Treaty of Versailles was signed in 1919, Albix was to be tried for treason, but he subsequently disappeared, and a heretofore unknown twin brother of his—Albis, who looked exactly like Albix but with a mustache—took the reins of the company.

His lack of moral compass notwithstanding, Albis turned out to have a head for business, and Sweetums continued its ascent, adding radio stations, TV stations, and newspapers to its holdings in order to counteract what had become a tidal wave of negative press. In 1933, flush with cash and looking to expand his empire, Albis founded a movie studio, churning out slapstick comedies and Wild West adventure movies. He also made several films that "were so racist they made *Birth of a Nation* look like *Malcolm X*."[18] In August of 1940, Albis threw a lavish red carpet premiere for his first directorial effort, *Gone With a Wind*, which was a shot-for-shot remake of *Gone With the Wind*, except the role of "Mammy," originally portrayed by Hattie McDaniel in her groundbreaking, Oscar™-winning performance, was played by Albis himself, in drag, fat suit, and blackface. He didn't even shave his mustache.[19]

Albix Newport and his "brother," Albis Newport.

---

[17] Professor Nedney Prosser, *Gumdrops, Lollypops, and Fascism: The Life of Albix Newport* (College Park, MD: University of Maryland Press, 1993).

[18] Professor Nedney Prosser, *Candycanes, Unicorns, and Bigotry: Corporate Adventures in Anti-Civil Rights Propaganda* (College Park, MD: University of Maryland Press, 1997).

[19] All copies of the movie were instantly burned, and no official record of the film exists. The only way we even know it happened is Albis's diary. "The film was not well-received," he wrote, "and it is hard to determine why that is so. Perhaps the audience was overly familiar with the original and tired of watching a remake. Or perhaps my performance was *too* good—so good that it frightened people. Indeed, this seems possible, as many who watched seemed not to even want to approach me afterwards, as if the power of my acting were intimidating them into silence. But no matter. I recently had an idea for a remake of *The Wizard of Oz*, in which I would play every part, in blackface."

The Sweetums building after its refurbishing in 1955. Nick Newport, who oversaw the remodel, told the architects: "This candy company needs a building that's imposing, daunting, brutalistic, and impenetrable."

Despite his critical, financial, moral, ethical, and basic-human-level failings, Albis Newport ran Sweetums for another decade, before his death at the age of eighty-two from a laudanum overdose. His oldest son, legendary Pawnee citizen, and Indiana's oldest man (as of this book's printing), Nick Newport, Sr., ascended to the Sweetums throne in 1949 and has presided over an unprecedented period of growth and expansion. In the ensuing decades, Sweetums branched into industries ranging from cupcakes to automated weapon triggers (*see sidebar, next page*). Nick Newport's success in business is rivaled only by his scandalous personal life. He has been married no fewer than eleven times, most recently to three-time Miss Pawnee Beauty Pageant winner Jessica Wicks, who is almost sixty years his junior. "I hope he lives forever," said Wicks recently, while lying.[20]

In 1975, Sweetums took advantage of its proximity to massive amounts of local corn and began using corn syrup instead of sugar. The amount of sweeteners used in their products is astonishing. Sweetums X-Treme Twisties are 70 percent sugar and sugar substitutes, while Frooties! brand soda is quite literally just a thirty-two-ounce can of high-fructose corn syrup. Attempts by heroic local activists to lower the amount of corn syrup in Sweetums products have so far met with no success. I will admit, though, Frooties! tastes *amazing*. I drink it while I work out, for energy.

Today, Sweetums is every bit as vital to the town's health as it is detrimental to our actual health. One in three Pawnee citizens is employed, directly or indirectly, by Sweetums and its many subsidiaries, so we support the company even as we acknowledge its many failings.[21] In many ways, Sweetums is Pawnee, and Pawnee is Sweetums. Or, as Albis Newport once famously remarked, "*La ville, c'est moi.*"[22]

---

[20] Shauna Malwae-Tweep, "Newport Celebrates 99th Birthday in Style," *Pawnee Journal*, April 21, 2010. I know I shouldn't editorialize, but come on, Jessica. Let's get real.

[21] In 2008, Sweetums' overseas business partners were discovered to employ massive numbers of unpaid children under the age of fourteen. The company has since donated several hundred dollars to the fight against child labor in Asia.

[22] Literally, "I am the city." The remarks were made at the 1941 Chamber of Commerce annual meeting, and ruffled more than a few feathers. Not for the statement, which, at that moment in time, was completely true. But rather because Albis spoke French, which no one understood.

Sweetums-Related Businesses

(Farm and Cattle Services)

- Beef 'Em Ups (corn-based cattle feed)
- Fix 'Em Ups (antibiotics for cattle)
- Prop 'Em Ups (kickstand cattle attachments for overmedicated cattle)
- Slice 'Em & Dice 'Ems (cattle slaughter-house blades and eviscerators)
- T-Bone Henderson's Casual Steakhouse Eateries

CornflowerGirl

- CornflowerGirl Cosmetics
- CornflowerGirl Extra-High-Alcohol Scotch Whiskey
- CornflowerGirl Corn-Based Asbestos Insulation
- CornflowerGirl Corn-Made Men's Casual Footwear

(Restaurant Supplies)

- Fry 'Ems (deep fryers, flash fryers, and instafryers)
- Corneo's (220,000 BTU decathlon tube flash fryers for corn products)
- CorneoPower, Inc. (high-BTU modification kits and generators for maximizing power from Corneo's brand flash fryers)
- Corbin Cornelius's Corn Cob Holders (those things with the two prongs that go into the corn; market capitalization: $2.3 billion)

MACHINE 'EMS

(Industrials)

- Uncle Jessums' Kidney Dialysis Machines
- BillyBob's Down-Home Southern-Fried Hostile Environment Personal Protective Bodyguard Services and Strikeforce Units (co-operated by Xe [formerly Blackwater])
- ChloroTech Chemical (including cadmium refineries and mercury treatment plants)
- KRP Automated Triggers
- Paulson Detonators
- QuickFire Triggers
- Hair's Breadth Weapon Triggers
- Ask Questions Later Automated Triggers
- PreëmptiveStrike Neutron Bomb Triggers
- Panacea Trigger Corp.
- Trigger-than-Life Handgun Triggers
- Itchy Finger Shotgun Triggers
- No Time to Think Mechanized Assault Rifle Triggers
- Second Amendment Assault Rifle Trigger Modification Kits
- OnePlanet Compact Fluorescent Lightbulbs

MISC.

- *Pawnee Journal* and *Sun* newspapers
- 16 FM and AM radio stations across southern Indiana and northwest Kentucky
- Dwight D. Eisenhower Memorial Library
- Conseco Field House
- University of Michigan
- Movie rights to the children's book *Goodnight Moon*
- Creepy Crawlies Spider Chow (food for spiders)

Sweetums Products

Fruityums
Chewy fruity candies

Icyums
Wintergreen gum

Frooties!
Soda pop (really just corn syrup)

Nutriyums [23] [24]
Health bars

Gusherz [25]
Nougat-filled chocolates

Nutz 'N Stuf
Candy snack mix with nuts, licorice bites, gummi bears, red hots, pretzels, and beef jerky nuggets

Jus' Stuf
Candy snack mix (just beef jerky nuggets and licorice)

Kandy Nailz
Candy fingernails (slogan: "Chewing on nails has never been such a delicious habit!")

Lil' Nooses
Licorice ropes

Puppy Pops
Dog bone–shaped shortbread biscuits for people

Poppy Pups
Bagel-shaped dog bones for dogs

Wateryums
Hard candy with refreshing water inside

Earring Pops
Earring-shaped candy (can actually pierce ears, contains metal)

Metalyums
Candy-scented eleven-inch industrial construction screws (not for consumption)

Nougat in Yo' Face
Facial cream (not for consumption)

Sweetums Peanut Butter
Not for consumption

Teef Saverz
Sugarfree gum

Teef Killerz
Extra-sugar gum

Mike and Plenty

Good and Ike

[23] Note from excellent and beautiful nurse Ann Perkins: "Do *not* eat Nutriyum Bars. They have enough sugar, corn syrup, fat, sodium, and preservatives to kill a horse."

[24] Note from Leslie Knope: "They also taste *amazing*. I eat them when I work out, for energy."

[25] See Appendix 4: Pawnee's 10 Worst Disasters.

Sweetums Fun Salt
Salt (high-fructose corn syrup-flavored salt)

Sweetums Delicious SnakPak
100-calorie snack packs

Sweetums Delicious SnackPak
1,000-calorie snack packs

SwimmyYums
Pan-roasted wild striped bass dipped in chocolate

High-Fructose Corn Syrup

Discontinued Products

Lithiyums
High-lithium fruit gummies

Morphyums
High-morphine Lithiyums

- **Low-fat Morphyums**
  Low-fat high-morphine Lithiyums

- **Morphyums Zero**
  High-morphine Lithiyums with zero calories

- **Edible Monocles**

- **Grandpa-Flavored Butterscotch Candies**

- **Marlyums**
  Smokeable candy cigarettes

- **"Bitter Memories" Brand Licorice**

- **White Chocolate Eggs**

- **Whites-Only Chocolate Eggs**

- **Whites-Only White Chocolate White-Butter Peanut Butter Cups for White People**

- **Taffy for Hispanics**

- **Bag of Acid**

- **Thimble o' Beef Stew**

- **Candy Actual-Canes**
  Intended for use as canes

- **Gumdrops 'N Hair**

- **Butt Lollipops**
  (theorized about, drawn up in the lab, oddly at one time considered for military applications, never actually produced)

Kernston's Rubber Nipples

George Kernston and his wife Cecilia settled in Pawnee in 1867, claiming a massive and valuable tract of land on Pawnee's eastern edge. In 1885, George built the **Kernston's Vulcanized Rubber Tire Factory**. That is the last good thing that happened to them, before what has become basically a 125-year crapstorm.

The well-documented "Kernston Curse" struck immediately, when some faulty machinery caused the tires to come off the assembly line in the shape of triangles. This explains the old company slogan, "Kernston Tires: Move Slower!" From there things only got worse—their factory burned down *eight* times over a forty-year period (two arsons, two passed-out cigarette smokers, three malfunctioning machines, and one "argument about how the first fire had started, which led to a reenactment of the first fire, which got out of hand and just turned into another fire"). More tragically, a seemingly endless stream of Kernstons have died before their time. *(See sidebar, right.)*

In 1974, after the untimely death of Emerson Max Kernston, the family shuttered many of their side businesses and focused on their most successful product: rubber nipples for baby bottles. They have been on a steady upswing ever since! Except for all of the weird and unlikely deaths and mishaps.

As much as I support the family and value

Cecilia Kernston was the original model for their famed rubber nipple.

The Kernston Curse—
Unnatural Deaths Abound

CORNELIUS KERNSTON (1899): struck by lightning as he fell off a steamboat.

FLETCHER KERNSTON (1914): drank a cup of poison he mistook for gin.

PHINNEAS AND ABIGAIL KERNSTON (1937): playing with jacks, they bumped their heads together so hard that their skulls fused. The surgery was successful, but eighteen years later the exact same thing happened again and they both died.

CECIL KERNSTON III (1946): fell asleep on a buzz saw during a blackout; then the power came back on.

LEONARD KERNSTON (1951): stepped on a crack in the road. His mother, Lucy, fell sideways over him and broke four vertebrae in her back. Then they were both struck by lightning.

JONATHAN W. KERNSTON IV (1973): trying to commit suicide, he drank a cup of gin he thought was poison, and drunkenly fell out a window and impaled himself on an umbrella stand as he was struck by lightning.

EMERSON MAX KERNSTON (1974): his sleeve got caught in a molding machine on the floor of the Kernston rubber factory, and he was sucked into the gears, ground into pieces, and forged into dozens of Subaru Outback floor mats.

MEG KERNSTON (1987): stabbed herself.

Julie Kernston was super-weird.

their role in Pawnee history, I still can't recommend you tour the factory. It just seems like you're asking for something awful to happen. The whole family really is kind of freaky—I went to high school with Julie Kernston, who wasn't even like one of the main ones, she was like a second cousin or something, and she was *weird*. She looked like a duck and last I heard she was like thirty and had never kissed a guy. I think she's in the Coast Guard or something.

LACEY CHUMBERLY

Like many of my customers, I was looking to make a change," said Lacey Chumberly, while snipping away at the bangs of one of her regulars. "I had just left Fantastic Sam's, and I wanted to cut out on my own—no pun intended." Chumberly fell in love with a cute little storefront at 217 Blue Jay Way, and opened up **Lacey's Place** in December of 2005.

"Things were really slow for, like, months," she recalled. "There were weeks where I'd be lucky if I got five people through the door, total." Lacey says she owes a lot of her business education to Earl Gardenhauser, who had run **Bark Avenue Pet Emporium** right across the street for fifteen years. "Earl pointed out that I didn't have the word 'salon' or 'hair' in the name, which meant it didn't pop up when people looked for salons on the Internet." So, in September 2006, Lacey's Place became the **Britney-Spears-MySpace-Hips-Don't-Lie-Video-WWE-World-Series-Paris-Hilton-Dick-Cheney-Shooting-Incident-Zidane-Headbutt-Ted-Haggard-Peyton-Manning-Upskirt-Videos Lacey's Place Salon**.

People aren't searching for MySpace or the video to Shakira's "Hips Don't Lie" as much as they once did, but Lacey says the salon's name will stay the same, since her regulars would get upset. Throw in the money she's spent on stationery, and the fact that her longtime receptionist finally nailed a version of their answering machine message where she's talking fast enough that she gets the whole name in before the beep, and the Britney-Spears-MySpace-Hips-Don't-Lie-Video-WWE-World-Series-Paris-Hilton-Dick-Cheney-Shooting-Incident-Zidane-Headbutt-Ted-Haggard-Peyton-Manning-Upskirt-Videos Lacey's Place Salon will be here for a long time!

Entertainment 720

Founded by Tom Haverford and Jean-Ralphio Saperstein, Entertainment 720 has been Pawnee's premiere entertainment conglomerate since mid-2011. If you have an entertainment need, they can deliver: audio systems, videos, nightclubs, promotion, VIP handling, parties, red carpet events, iPhone apps, celebrity appearances[26], piano lessons . . . they do it all. Come visit their b-a-n-a-n-a-s HQ at 602 Trumball Street. They'll go around the world twice for their clients!

Salons with Hair-Related Puns in Their Names

There's a reason this city was called "PUNnee" in the Southwest Indiana Office of Economic Development's last annual report.[27] Nowhere is the Pawnee business community's proclivity for wordplay more apparent than the many salons and barbershops that use puns in their names. So, without further a-"do," "hair" are my favorites!

An Aff-hair to Remember (783 Proctor Street)
According to Trim (222 Howell Drive)
Hair Necesse-Tease (19 Wilkie Way)
From Hair to Epermity (290 Howell Drive)
Hairy and the Handersons Cuts and Manicures (238 Howell Drive)
There's No Business Like Haircut Business (224 Howell Drive)

Bob and Weave (151 Elton Street)
Star Wars, Episode V: The Hairpire Strikes Back (225 Howell Drive)
The Assassination of Your Too-Long Bangs by the Coward Gina Veramopolis[28] (232 Howell Drive)
Hairspray[29] (10 Coltenberry Way)

[26] Celebrities for celebrity appearances currently limited to former NBA great Detlef Schrempf and Walt Saperstein, Pawnee's most recognizable (from his bus ads) ophthalmologist.

[27] Full disclosure: mostly, that reason is that I wrote the official report on Pawnee's business climate, and I love puns.

[28] For those of you who don't know, this is a parody of the 2007 feature film *The Assassination of Jesse James by the Coward Robert Ford*, starring Brad Pitt. I use the word "parody" loosely. As, apparently, does salon owner Gina Veramopolis. The "come up with a pun name for your hair salon based on a famous movie title" arms race that has been waged on the 200 block of Howell Drive in the last eight years is like a whole other book entirely.

[29] Not 100 percent sure this is a reference to the theatrical musical and movie entitled *Hairspray*, but it's at least possible, so I'm throwing it in.

April's Guide to HIPSTER PAWNEE

Hi. I'm April. So you want to experience something "hip"? Okay. Get in your **car**. Go to the nearest **airport**. That will be the **Pawnee Airport**, because it is the only airport. Walk up to the ticket counter and buy a ticket. Doesn't matter where. The only planes that fly out of there are those little **rickety scary planes** that look like they're going to fall apart when someone like even **sneezes**, but they can fly you away from here so it's worth it. Get on one and tell the guy to fly you **anywhere**. You can be in Indianapolis in like an hour—just do it, and then from there get on a plane to a **real city** with real people and real things to do.[30]

If there are no flights, I guess you can go to this one vintage store in Pawnee called **Glen's Closet**. Unfortunately Glen sucks and so does his closet.[31] Everything smells

like mothballs and corn chips. On the rare occasion there is something kind of cool that comes in, the girls that work there get all the best stuff. Whatever.

After Glen's Closet, the coolest thing in Pawnee is the **garbage dump** and I'm not even kidding. It's a huge garbage dump filled with (a) weird trash from all the freaks who live here, and (b) like a billion raccoons.

After the garbage dump, in terms of "hipness," literally everything else in the entire town is **tied for last**.

Find one of these things and fly away from here.

---

[30] She is kidding. She loves Pawnee, and she is happily married to a great guy, and she secretly loves her job as assistant to Ron Swanson, and the only reason I am letting her put this in my book is because I want her to see how silly she looks when this is printed.

[31] This part I agree with—that place sucks.

TERRY PORTER

Pawnean **Terry Porter** started collecting wigs at the age of six. Now forty-one, he has acquired one of the Midwest's largest private-citizen wig collections! Terry has over **one thousand wigs** on display in his home, which he shares with his mother, Gladys Porter, and his "Grammy," Edna Porter. **Porter's House of Wigs** (888 Kilroy St.) is one of Pawnee's most popular tourist attractions. Are you a **blonde** and wondered what you'd look like as a **brunette**? Well now you can stop wondering. Remember to bring your **camera**!

(Open 11 A.M.–3 P.M., Tuesdays to Wednesdays. Please do not attempt to try on Grammy Edna's actual wig. This upsets Terry greatly, and he has been known to just boot everyone out and sulk in a corner.)

Pawnee's Best Ethnic Restaurants

If you're looking for something a little exotic, Pawnee has what you crave. So grab your passport and prepare to be whisked away to a foreign land of deliciousness!

Pete's Petezaria 677 Wamapoke Drive
This authentic Italian restaurant was opened in 2009 by 3-star (on Yelp) chef, Pete Oglini. Try a slice of his famous Pete-za or his delicious four-cheese lasagn-pete.

Food and Stuff 729 Glenmore Blvd.
More a grocery store than a restaurant, they have all the ingredients you'll need to prepare a meal at home that will whisk you away to an exotic foreign land. They also have a variety of household products, garden supplies, industrial tubing, and lead-based paints.

Indiana Fred's 444 State Street
Indiana Cuisine at its most Indianian. The corn is a must-try!

Taco Bell (Various locations)
Mexico called—it wants its delicious cuisine back. Feeling especially adventurous? Order the Enchirito. You'll feel so Mexican, you'll want to attack the Alamo!

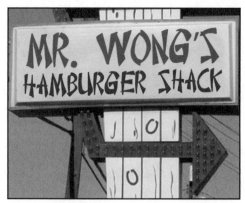

North Indie's 1990 Route 37
Nothern Indiana food the way Northern Indianans do it best. Don't leave without trying the corn.

Mr. Wong's Hamburger Shack
91 Sunderland
The best hamburgers in town.

JJ's Diner 122 Sunderland
Every day is *French* toast day. I still
have to recommend the waffles,
though. (Also, even though this is the
"ethnic" food section, do *not* get the
Belgian waffles. Just awful.)

Wamapoke Brewery, 19 Penbury Lane
Pawnee's Own Local Beer

Starting in 1928, Pawnee began celebrating quittin' time by tossing back a few locally brewed Wamapoke Ales. For decades, their famous laughing squaw logo was probably the most recognizable in town, and easily the most offensive. Then, in 1959, the Hoosier Mart opened up on Racine Blvd. (the town's first true supermarket), and they carried all the big brands—Bud, Miller High Life, you name it. And people suddenly realized something: Wamapoke Ale was absolutely horrible.[32]

Despite the sudden influx of actually potable beer, Wamapoke Ale continued to sell pretty well. Perhaps it was already ingrained into our culture, or perhaps it was easier for kids to buy a sixer of 'Poke from a convenience store without proper ID than it was to get Miller from the Hoosier Mart. Whatever the case, to this day if you head into the woods behind the closed-down mini-golf place, you're sure to see only one brand of broken bottle.

Apparently the beer also sells extremely well in some parts of Brooklyn.

[32] A popular playground parody of their jingle went thus: "Wamapoke Ale / Worse than jail / Drink a few / Tastes like poo."

Why not relax a little while you're in town at **SPAwnee** (622 Holber Street)—Pawnee's number one/only place for relaxing massages and facials. Close your eyes, ignore the odd smellscape, and relax!

SPAWNEE TREATMENT MENU

4-HOUR FACIAL

Bye-bye kids—have fun with the sitter. Mom and/or Dad is about to experience a sixth of a day getting the kind of soothing facial treatment we all could use now and again. Need a longer vacation? Buy back-to-back 4-hour facials, or even better, book our three-day Facial Retreat, where you get sixteen hours of facials a day and sleep in an RV trailer parked behind the spa. (Sleeping bag not provided.) (Facial: $40, 3-Day Retreat: $400)

SWEET 'N' SOUR FACIAL

A soothing treatment using the Oriental secrets of Chinese food seasoning. This one generally tends to sting—we recommend you book on a Saturday morning and block out some alone time afterwards, out of the eye of society. The next day, your skin will be tender to the touch, and a "greasy" look is normal for a few weeks. But an hour after you get one, you'll want another! ($50)

COUNTRY FACIAL

Does it smell like BBQ sauce? It is, partly! A Spawnee favorite. ($18)

FULL BODY MASSAGE

Lie back and let our trained professionals rub all your cares away. Our state-of-the-art military-grade cots provide the comfort, and a Sharper Image–imitation sound machine will emit a sound of crashing waves that is basically indistinguishable from real crashing waves. Your whole body will thank you! ($110)

NOTE: Due to a pending lawsuit, we legally cannot massage anything below the shoulders or above the knees, you must be sitting fully upright, and a third party must be present.[33]

---

[33] In case that wasn't clear, this is a $110 shoulder massage with a cop watching.

"SWEDISH" DEEP-TISSUE MASSAGE

Just added to our menu this week! For the true massage junkie, here's the intense stress-reliever you're looking for. Our staff has been reading up on this hard-core, sometimes painful technique, and although they have never attempted it, they are eager to try. Let one of our staff grind away your cares, really just going to town on your muscles and bones and so forth with their bony elbows, or however they do it, putting massive amounts of directed pressure right on the tenderest areas of your back, neck, stomach (we think?), and legs. Maybe don't do this if you're pregnant. Give it a shot and see what happens! (Free, for anyone willing to let us try it out on them to see if we can do it.)

D.I.Y. COUPLES MASSAGE

Bring your loved one and relax as you massage one another. ($125)

HAY AND MUD BODY SCRUB

Learn what horses have known for centuries . . . the healing power of Indiana mud and the exfoliating properties of plain old American dry hay. You will be rolled in mud and hay like a horse. ($10)

BLIND PLEASURES

Remove one of the senses, and the others go on overdrive. Experience the sensual pleasures of our Blindfold Massage. Every touch, every sensation is heightened, leading to a world of incredible relaxation. ($100. $150 if you want to be blindfolded, too.)

IT'S ELECTRIC

Let your cares disappear into thin air as our trained staff walks around in their socks and then zaps you with their static-y fingers. ($75)

HOT TUB

You can go in our hot tub for eight bucks. ($8)

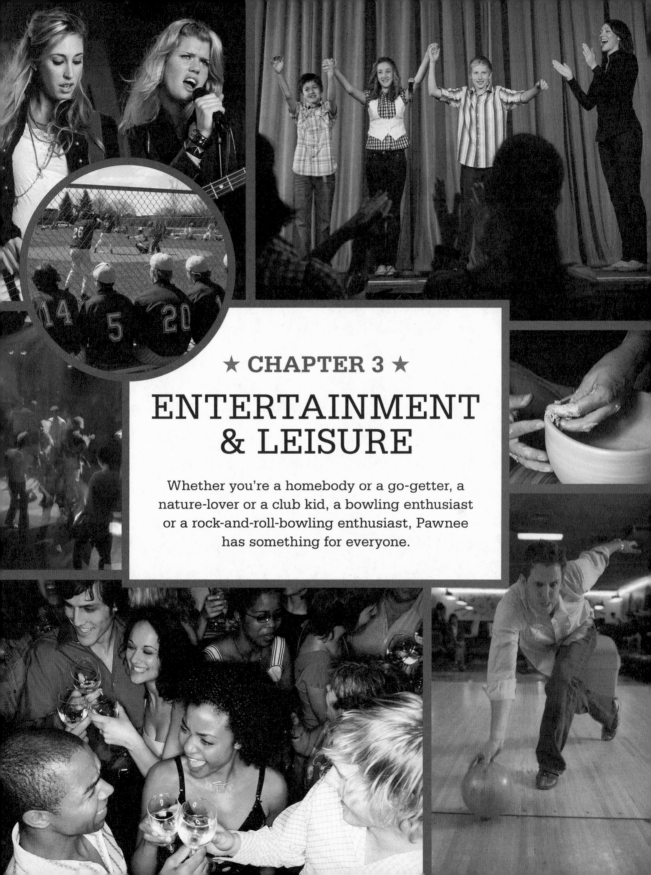

★ CHAPTER 3 ★

ENTERTAINMENT & LEISURE

Whether you're a homebody or a go-getter, a nature-lover or a club kid, a bowling enthusiast or a rock-and-roll-bowling enthusiast, Pawnee has something for everyone.

3

The Best Concert Venues in Pawnee

by Andy Dwyer

I'm in a band called Mouse Rat, which you definitely would know about if you lived in Pawnee. We're amazing. Most people describe us as a cross between Dave Matthews, Bruce Springsteen, and a third, other band that doesn't exist but is amazing.

We have had the pleasure of playing in every corner of this entire city and blowing the doors off of those corners. In my opinion, every venue is awesome if you're getting a chance to rock out, but here are some of my personal favorite places for watching live music:

Paladino's

Paladino's is the cream of the crop. Kickass venue, great sound system, good crowds. Plus they pay you in free drinks! What more could you want? Also, you can play forever. They'll literally never stop you from playing. One night, we had eleven encores. People were so drunk they didn't recognize that six of the eleven were the same song because we had run out of songs.

Side note: Mouse Rat won the WKKR 2008 Battle of the Bands at Paladino's, though you might not know that because at the time we were called Scarecrow Boat.

Ann Perkins's House

One time when Ann and I were dating, she went to work and we had a concert there. When she came home, there were like a million people in her backyard. She was mad at first, but then I told the band, "I know exactly what to do, guys. Let's play Ann's favorite song."

It *immediately* did not work. She kicked everyone out including me. So I would recommend to other bands not to play impromptu concerts at Ann's house.

Side note: That concert was actually reviewed the next day, in the *Pawnee Journal*! It was in the police blotter section, because this crappy neighbor of Ann's named Lawrence called the cops on us. But it was the first time a band I was in ever got a review in the paper.

Side side note: The band at the time was called Ninja Dick, so if you're looking it up in the archives or whatever, search for "ninja dick ann's house impromptu concert cops called andy music awesome cops" or something, and it will definitely show up.

Pawnee Public Access Channel 46

We played for the diabetes telethon, and it was awesome. Not only did we get exposure, but we were also doing a good thing, because deep down I believe music is a gift to everyone's ears. It was great exposure. Do you have any idea how many people saw us?! I'd love to know. I want to put the number on our website.

Side note: One article that was written about the telethon accidentally referred to us as "Scrotation Marks," because at the time I was thinking about changing the band name to "Scrotation Marks" and I wrote down on this piece of paper that that's what we were called.

You know what? Let me just go ahead right now and list every single name the band has ever been called, so you can look us up throughout the course of history:

Mouse Rat

Scarecrow Boat

Malice in Chains

Punch Face Champion

Flames for Flames

Taint Champion

Two Doors Down

The Andy Andy Andys

Andy and the D-Bags

Lance Armstrong's Uniball

Crackfinger (Andy Dwyer Solo Project)

God Hates Figs

Department of Homeland Obscurity

Fourskin

Magnum B.M. (Andy Dwyer Solo Project)

Puppy Pendulum

Possum Pendulum

Penis Pendulum

Ben Franklin and the Electric Keys

Radwagon

Jet Black Pope

Beatles McJagger

Majestic Erection

Butt Cup (Andy Dwyer Solo Project)

Scanning for Viruses

Balls of the Sun

Empire of the Balls

Pet Bible

Muscle Confusion

Worm Police

Just the Tip (Andy Dwyer Solo Project)

Ape Syphilis

Fiveskin

Threeskin

Angel Snack

Nothing Rhymes with Orange

Everything Rhymes with Orange

Nothing Rhymes with Blorange

Ninja Dick

Scrotation Marks

. . . And You Will Know Us By Our
   Amazing Trail Mix

Dry Hump (Andy Dwyer Solo Country
   Music Project)

Catastrophe Diverted

Shark in the Toilet

Sweatpants Boner

The Assassination of Andy Dwyer by
   the Coward Robert Ford

Okay—I think that's all of them.
   Back to the thing.

Edward Phillips Senior Center

You always have to know your audience, and this audience was super-old people. We played on Valentine's Day, so we played mostly these old songs that did whatever the opposite of "rocking out" is. Usually, if we play a love song and people start making out, that's a good sign. But I did not want to see those people making out. Sorry, but it was gross, and I stand by that. Luckily, they didn't make out. They just seemed to dig it, and seven women gave me their granddaughters' phone numbers.

The Lot Behind Ann Perkins's House

There's a big empty lot behind Ann's house that Leslie is trying to turn into a park, and we have had a bunch of events there. I played a kickass song called "5000 Candles in the Wind" at the Li'l Sebastian Memorial Thing last spring, and there was literally not a dry eye in the lot. Also, I was supposed to play a show there after this dude Freddy Spaghetti canceled—which totally goes against the rocker's code. You *never* cancel a show,

unless you get hit by a car. Which is what happened to me. So I had to cancel, but I totally have an excuse. I was super disappointed, but this was also the day I got kissed by April Ludgate, making it the most awesome day *ever*.

So I guess you could say . . . the best place to play music in Pawnee . . . *is your heart.*

Don't steal that line. I'm totally using that as a lyric.

The Solitude of Nature: A Diary

by Ron Swanson

A picture of me.

Hello. I am Ron Swanson. Leslie has asked me to contribute to this book. I told her I was not interested one hundred times and she kept right on asking. I have worked with her long enough to know that this means I have to do whatever the thing is that she has asked me to do. Once she asked me for permission to hire a mime troupe to perform at the community center, and I told her she could not, and she sent the mimes to follow me around for the entire day and pretend they were crying, ostensibly because of my cruelty. Another time I told her she could not create a "double-Dutch jump rope club"(?) in a park, and she sat cross-legged on my desk for thirty hours. Dammit, I'm getting angry just remembering these things.

She also does all my work for me—not because I ask her to, just because she wants to, and I do not—so I owe her a lot of favors, so I will contribute to this book. She suggested several articles I had no interest in writing. I countered by suggesting that instead of writing any of those articles, I would simply go to my cabin in the woods for a month and pretend our conversation had never happened. She got very excited and told me that this was an excellent idea, because then I could write of my experiences "off the beaten path" in Pawnee. "Like Thoreau at Walden Pond!" she squealed. I told her Thoreau actually went home every night he was "living" at Walden Pond (true—look it up), and that I thought that made him kind of a pussy. She told me to watch my language and that I had one month to turn in my diary. And now here we are.

One Month Living in the Woods In Pawnee
by Ron Swanson

Typed on an Underwood 5 typewriter with original carriage return that I found in a dumpster and completely restored.

DAY 1 I am in my cabin in the woods. It's good. No one else is around for 2 miles in any direction. I have some water and whiskey and my shotgun. I am going to go kill my dinner. Okay I am back and I have my dinner, a deer. I shot this deer and now I will cook it.

DAY 1, LATER I cooked and ate the deer flank and it was very gamey. But the whiskey is good.

DAY 1, LATER I drank most of the whiskey and I'm hungry again so I am going to eat more of the deer.

DAY 1, LATER I ate more of the deer and it was less gamey than I remembered. I also had more whiskey.

Day 1, LATER I am just sitting here.

DAY 1, LATER More deer has been eaten by me. It is very good deer meat.

DAY 1, LATER The rest of the deer is about to have been eaten by me. Also I drank the rest of the whiskey. I underestimated how much whiskey I would need out here. I will probably have to go to the store to buy more whiskey. I didn't want to leave this cabin at all, but what the hell, Thoreau left Walden Pond every day he was writing that book. It is taking me a long time to type this because I am eating more of the deer with one of my hands. This is the best deer meat I have ever eaten. Thank you, deer, for being so delicious. I will eat the rest of you soon and use your antlers as decoration in my cabin if there is any room left on my walls. I am looking around and seeing that there is not. Every wall has deer antlers on every available inch of wall. Sorry, deer.

DAY 1, LATER Okay I am going to bed, in this chair.

DAY 2 I just woke up in this chair. I am reading over what I wrote yesterday about my day. What a fantastic day that was. Reading about my day really took me back to how good that deer was, and the whiskey. I am getting hungry. I'll be right back. Okay I am back and I have eight rabbits. I am going to cook one of the rabbits and eat it for breakfast. Okay, I have cooked one of the rabbits. It tastes good.

DAY 2, LATER I feel as though this diary is going really well. I will be very proud to send it to Leslie for her review. I am going to send these first pages to her to make sure that this is what she is looking for. This will also afford me the ability to stop writing for a few days and just concentrate on the things that I want to do.

DAY 6 I heard back from Leslie. She says that what I have written is excellent. She also encouraged me to be a bit more descriptive. "Some adjectives wouldn't hurt," she said. She also said that I didn't have to necessarily record everything I do at every moment. She then reiterated several times that what I had written so far was excellent. She specifically said that I should be "very proud of myself" and that I am a "wonderful man and a fine writer." She also enclosed a sample of something she had written, that was "maybe more in line with what kind of thing I'm looking for." I will reprint it for you here:

> As the sun shyly peeks over the horizon, pouring its warmth over the serene silence of my rustic cabin, the distinctive call of a Black-Bellied Whistling Duck fills my ears with song and my heart with joy for the day of silent contemplation that lies ahead. My mind cannot help but drift back to the days of the first settlers here--nay, back further, when the gentle Wamapoke ruled, or back further still, when "America" was but an idea and democracy a mere promise of--

You see what I am dealing with.

She then said several more times that I was an excellent writer, and enclosed several bottles of whiskey, because she is thoughtful. I am going to consider what she said and try to maybe split the difference.

DAY 17 I haven't written anything in days because every time I sit down and imagine trying to write the way she suggested I grind my teeth together and my jaw starts to hurt.

DAY 19 I have no food tonight because I was about to take down a delicious-looking 170-inch Indiana Whitetail but I started thinking about how I could write about the experience in a way that Leslie would like and I lost my concentration and it ran away.

DAY 23 In the morning, a beautiful sunrise happened. It was outside and I saw it and it was beautiful. The sun rose up and everything got nice and the light was beautiful. There is a beautiful pond near my cabin and the water looked beautiful as the light doth shone o'er the water, and a bird went by and it was excellent and I thought about history and America oh Christ this is pointless. Writing ruins everything.

DAY 29 I am packing it in and just heading home. Here's why: the point of this isn't to write about it. The point of doing it is just to do it. I like being out here by myself. It's great. I like Pawnee because Pawnee is a town where there are stores and restaurants and whatnot, but also a decent chunk of it isn't developed--it's just forest and land and you can be by yourself like in this cabin I bought for $2200 fifteen years ago and just sit here and be happy. I've lived in Pawnee for 35 years and I wouldn't want to live anywhere else, because there are places in this town where I can see people I like or at least tolerate and there are places where I can sit in a cabin by myself and eat venison and drink whiskey and not talk to anyone which I like to do. Pawnee is a nice town, not too big or small, not too big for its britches, and there are deer I can shoot, and that's all I need.

DAY 30 I just got back and handed this to Leslie and told her she should just throw it away or do whatever she wanted, and she read it and got oddly emotional and said it was "perfect." So, goodbye.

A Gentlemen's (Club) Agreement

Transplants to Pawnee usually find themselves asking two questions: "Why are there five separate streets called Howell Drive?" and "How can a city this small have so many strip clubs?" While the first question has no easy answer,[34] the answer to the second question is "If only you'd been here eight years ago!"

In 2003, entrepreneur/pornographer Bert Schlaegle applied for a permit to open a gentleman's club he wanted to call "**Slutz**." People were outraged. There was no way the community would stand for that, as there already was a gentleman's club called Slutz. At the time, Pawnee already had the dubious distinction of having the highest strip club–per–citizen ratio in the United States. Strip clubs and strip club–affiliated businesses made up 17 percent of our total economy.[35] But a conservative wind was blowing through the country at the time, and it filled the sails of Republican city council member Donnie Tremble, who decided he had seen enough.[36]

On one side of this fierce battle: the culturally ascendant forces of social conservatism. On the other: Schlaegle, owner of the **Bottom Drawer** (Indiana's only bottomless nightclub) and president of the Pawnee Chamber of Commerce. During the city council meeting of October 29, 2003, Schlaegle made his case. Heated words were exchanged. Feelings were hurt. Sixty thousand dollars in property damage was done.

Finally, a compromise was struck. Schlaegle could expand his smut empire, but strict new zoning regulations were imposed that forced the relocation or closure of several clubs. These included **Dirty Girlz** (which was no longer allowed to share space with Jump Start Pre-School) and the **Greazy Polez** (which had to move out of the Stephens Street fire station). In exchange, several clubs (not coincidentally, all with owners or investors on the city council) were allowed to expand and extend their hours of operation. The club owners did make one final concession, however: they agreed to a new ordinance that required that "all adult entertainment facilities must have names worthy of Pawnee's young women." So, Slutz became **Talent and Poise**, the Bottom Drawer became the **Glitter Factory**, and **69 Trampz 69** became **Empowerment**. So. Yay. Progress.

Anyway, though I would prefer everyone just forget all about these stupid places, and while even writing the history of this whole affair has made me want to go volunteer as a career counselor at an all-girls school, I do have to add one thing: do *not* confuse the **"Glitter Factory"** (the strip club) with the **"Glitter Factory"** (the actual factory that makes glitter and children's party supplies). Their identical names are made all the more confusing because each is located at **750 Howell Drive**, but **different Howell Drives**.

[34] Obviously, the streets in question are named after city founder Reverend Luther Howell, but why there are five of them is anyone's guess. And it is completely confusing. Especially if you're trying to give someone directions to the Pierce Street entrance to the Pawnee Zoo, which are: make a left from Howell Drive onto Howell Drive, bear right on Blackstone Boulevard, then make a U-Turn on Howell Drive to get into the roundabout which will dump you out on Howell Drive going in the right direction.

[35] For example, Patsy's Pasties and Pole Wax was our thirteenth largest employer at the time.

[36] Quite literally. His monthly tab at Neon Dreamz was upward of $700.

Jean-Ralphio's Five Hottest Clubs in Pawnee

Hello, ladies.

What up READER!!!? It's your boy Jean-Ralphio, aka JR, aka Money in the Bank, giving you an EXCLUSIVE look at the five hottest clubs in Pawnee! You may want to put a helmet on . . . because this nonsense is gonna BLOW YOUR MIND!!!!!!!!!!!!!

5 PHARAOH'S DILEMMA Underage? Not a problem! I've seen sixteen-year-old girls get into the Dilemma by flashing a Blockbuster Video card. The dance floor in this place is straight bananas. The largest in Pawnee. Tommy Haverford and I have pulled amazing numbers by mowing it down. To "mow it down," you start on one side of the dance floor and attempt to hook up with every girl in your path until you get to the other side of the floor. Once completed, you turn around and reflect on all the females you've just conquered. Extra points if you drink a Vodka Lemonade while reflecting. Every time T and I finish mowing, the grass is HELLA GREEN!

> **GIB*:**
>
> Tessa: 5   Chilaque: 6
> Simantha: 5

4 DUI Oh, what up doll, I didn't see you there . . . at the dopest club in Pawnee that encourages drinking over the legal limit!!! What is that . . . ? Could it be . . . ? YES—the bar *is* made of crashed car bumpers. The seats? Inflated airbags. Tom and I once walked into this club, got hammered off of Rémy Martins, and did the entire dance

*(**G**irls **I**'ve **B**anged [at this club]) and their official hotness score

57

routine from "Thriller" to James Taylor's "Fire and Rain." We had to FIGHT OFF the panties thrown at our faces! !

GIB:

Gabby: 4 Simantha: 5

3 **CHEAP DREAMS** This club has TWO LEVELS! Which means while women are dancing on the first floor, TomTom and I are on the second floor strategizing like vultures over hot, drunken prey! If you are good at the board game Risk, this is the club for you. This place has got tight music, tight dresses, and tight architecture. The building was constructed in 1920 as a hospital for disfigured soldiers. These American heroes are immortalized on beautiful marble sculptures throughout the club. Also, from the second floor, you can see down girls' shirts! BOOM BOOM POW!!!

GIB:

Samantha: 6 Carly: 4

Jan: 5 Simantha: 5

2 **XX** It's time to play the percentages . . . at the third-largest lesbian club in Indiana! 98 percent women in this piece! Someone's bound to be pissed enough at their girlfriend(s), that they give T-Havey and me a shot! Also, the music in this club is *stupid* good! Club remixes of Natalie Merchant, Indigo Girls, and Paula Cole songs! Come thirsty for neon drinks with tons of exotic fruit in them, cuz that's all they got! (They also have some beers.) Important MVP note—DO NOT dress up as one of the Village People when going to XX, it's not considered funny nor ironic at a lesbian club.

GIB: N/A

1 SNAKEHOLE LOUNGE There can only be one king. One Paul Walker. One *Fast and the Furious* of clubs. Welcome to the SNAKEHOLE LOUNGE!!! The judges' scores are in: Music—10! Ladies—10! Drinks—10! Your Fantasies Coming True—10! 10! 10! There is no hotter club on planet Earth. It's as if God molded this club out of sex, Rémy Martin, and Adam's other rib! (Check out their dope Signature Drink Menu on the next couple of pages.) There is no reason to even read about other clubs. If the Snakehole is open, GO THERE IMMEDIATELY. If it's not, WAIT ON LINE COMIC-CON STYLE UNTIL THAT SHIZZ OPENS UP!!! If you are between the ages of eighteen and forty-five, tell them Jean-Ralphio sent you and get a free SnakeJuice and kiss in the VIP area (kiss pending, based on hotness level).

GIB

Lezlie: 10

Melanie: 10

Tammy: 10

Madison: 10

Madison L.: 10

Madison G.: 10

Colleena: 10

Jennie: 10

Oh schnapps I forgot about Madison K.: 10

Saldry: 10

Mamka: 10

Franny: 10

Simantha: 5

(but she looked like a 10 in the Snakehole's excellent lighting)

Eleanor: 10

Jiji: 10

That's it readers. The five hottest clubs in Pawnee. Now go work the field like crafty veterans! Just remember, TommyTCell and I are professionals, so your numbers will most definitely vary. Also . . . watch out for a girl named Simantha. She's *crazy*. For real.

snakehole lounge
Signature Drink Menu

SAND-GRIA
Exotic Spanish-style wine'n'fruit beverage with a sandy sugar bottom—don't worry it's not sand, it's sugar![37] Served with a drink umbrella.

By the glass: $7.50

Pitcher: $8.50

MARGAR-HOOHAS
Our house Margaritas, geared for the Ladies! Choose from Strawberry, Cherry, Berry-berry, Cotton Candy, Bubble Gum, Chocolate, Vanilla, Blueberry, Sugarberry, Cinnamon Apple, Yellowcake, Chocolate Fondue, Boysen-apple, Syrup-Berry, Cream, Berry Berry Berry, Pink, Marshmallow Oreo Cookie Double Chocolate Maple Walnut Strawberry Jelly Mystery Surprise, and Regular.

Most Flavors: $8.00

Marshmallow Oreo Cookie Double Chocolate Maple Walnut Strawberry Jelly Mystery Surprise[38]

$28.00

HIM-OSA
Dudes—are your ladies estrogening-it-up with all their Margar-hoohas? Order a Him-osa—a Mimosa for dudes only! It's a classic Mimosa, dyed black with food coloring and topped off with a sour cream—filled potato skin.

$8.00

FIRST DATE
A pint glass full of ice-cold vodka. Fight your way through that painful "get-to-know-you" portion of a first date. If it's going well, come back for seconds!

$7.50 2 for $12.00

POMEGRANATE BEER
A bottle of Miller Lite with pomegranate in it.

$3.50

ISLAND LIVIN'
A bottle of Miller Lite with pomegranate in it and a tiny umbrella.

$7.50

---

[37] Note from Ann Perkins: I've had this drink and I'm pretty sure that's sand.

[38] Note from Ann Perkins: The only "mystery" is what color your vomit will be.

snakehole
lounge
Signature Drink Menu

INDYTINI
A classic Martini, made by a real Indiana bartender and served right here in Indiana.

$20.00
(price includes $12.00 Authenticity Surcharge)

INDY 500
Our version of Long Island Iced Tea, comprised of 500 different alcohols and liquors. Do you accept the challenge?[39]

$17.00

VODKA CUCUMBER SALAD
A vodka-soaked cucumber salad, served as a side dish in a bowl with a multipurpose spork, which has also been soaked in vodka.

$12.00

MEDUSA'S REVENGE
A spicy brew of rum and sriracha hot sauce, served with multiple straws for sharing or speedy solo consumption.

$12.00
First five straws are free, $1.00 per additional straw.

SWEETUMS FIZZZ
Mandarin orange–flavored vodka, club soda, SleepBusterz Energy Drink, and eight shots of Sweetums Corn Syrup, topped with five maraschino cherries. A favorite of VIPs and high rollers.

$8.00
50¢ surcharge for each additional cherry.

RIMMERS
Any of the above drinks rimmed with your choice of: salt, sugar, cocoa powder, cayenne pepper, nacho cheese, garlic salt, sour cream, whipped cream, cream cheese, pie filling, BBQ sauce, mayonnaise, balsamic vinegarette, creamed spinach.

$1.00
per Rimmer.
Mix five for $4.00!

---

[39] Note from Ann Perkins: Please do not accept this challenge. I still work part-time as a nurse and people "accepting the challenge" has led to some truly terrible overnight shifts.

The Pawnee Players

Christmas[40] is a wonderful time of year here in Pawnee, from the Festival of Lights[41] in Ramsett Park to the traditional memorial ceremony for those lost in stampedes during Black Friday sales. But Christmas wouldn't be Christmas without a trip to the Agnes Porter Theater[42] to see the Pawnee Players in action!

Every December since 1989, the town's only theater company has performed its traditional version of *A Christmas Carol* to packed houses. Families come from all over the state, buying their tickets months in advance to the perpetually sold-out shows. "We know exactly what the audience wants," says T.P.P. artistic director Eustace Tiberghien. "The same exact production, of the same exact play, performed at the same exact place, year after year after year."

The *Christmas Carol* performances make up 96 percent of the theater's annual revenue. "I learned many years ago that without Tiny Tim there would be no Uncle Vanya, there would be no Hedda Gabler, no Willy Loman," Tiberghien said, "so, maybe ten years ago, I embraced it. I realized that six weeks of suffering through eight dreary shows a week meant that for the rest of the season, we could do the theater *we* wanted to do." Tiberghien then teared up a little, before quickly recovering, dabbing his eyes delicately with his monogrammed pashmina shawl. "So, if casting the 'actress,'" he spat, with air quotes, "Vivica B. Fox,[43] or Joan Callamezzo[44] from that *Pawnee Today* show means we can produce vital, experimental, boundary-pushing art for the rest of the year, then so be it."

The Pawnee Players' season runs from May through December, with a Summerstage performance at Ramsett Park during the first week in July. So what are you waiting for? Hop online and get tickets to *A Christmas Carol*! (For all other performances to all other plays, you can pretty much just walk in. You should also probably drink a cup of coffee first and maybe bring a magazine or something.)

---

[40] Last year, Councilman Dexhart led a crusade to ban the use of the phrase "Happy Holidays" on city property. At the press conference, he declared victory over those waging "The War Against Christmas" as well as "The War Against Easter," which no one was aware was happening.

[41] At a separate press conference, Dexhart also declared war on Chanukah. His first act of aggression was annexing the phrase "Festival of Lights" for use during the Ramsett Park Christmas display. Dexhart insisted he wasn't anti-Semitic, he just thinks "Jewish people's holidays are illegitimate in the eyes of Jesus and America." The notoriously promiscuous Dexhart further announced the formation of a commission charged with assessing the feasibility of a War on Herpes.

[42] See the "Other Pawnee Feminist Pioneers" section (page 143) for more on Ms. Porter, a personal heroine of mine. In addition to her many achievements in the field of medicine, she was also the first Pawneean to attend a Broadway show, which is why our only professional theater bears her name.

[43] Vivica B. Fox (no relation) is a Pawnee native who played the role of "Woman Reluctant to Order Biggie Fries" in a Wendy's commercial in 1993.

[44] See Chapter 8, "Local Media," for much more on Ms. Callamezzo. In addition to her role as Pawnee's number one most trusted name in entertainment, she is a three-time Ghost of Christmas Present, two-time Mrs. Cratchit, and did one unfortunate performance as "Sexy Tiny Tim."

The Pawnee Players

2011–2012 Season

SCHOOL FOR WIVES *May 16 to June 9*
Molière's crowd-pleasing, comic tour de force! Translated from the original
French into sparkling, lively, contemporary Basque.

THE COAST OF UTOPIA TRILOGY *June 12 to August 23*
Sir Tom Stoppard's contemporary classic is presented in its entirety. This performance
will feature Pawnee Players' Artistic Director Eustace Tiberghien playing all of the
roles except Belinsky's Mistress, which will be visually represented by a taxidermied
hawk and voiced by Eustace Tiberghien. Please note that the eight-hour production will
be presented without intermission or bathroom access.

A MAN WITHOUT QUALITIES, PARTS 1–7 *August 25 to October 14*
The World Premiere of Artistic Director Eustace Tiberghien's adaptation of Robert
Musil's wonderful (if criminally infrequently read) multithousand-page tale of Vienna
before the Great War. Part 1 will be performed on Mondays, Part 2 on Tuesdays, etc.
Each part will run for four hours, except Part 6, which has been broken into two parts,
Part 6 Part 1 (Saturdays, 10AM–2PM) and Part 6 Part 2 (Saturday nights, 6PM–
11:45PM). If you want to skip certain parts, please arrive prepared to take a test on
the content and thematic elements of the parts you are skipping in order to be granted
admission to whichever part you want to see.

DE SHREEUW (Limited Engagement) *October 19 to November 4*
Direct from the Nijmejen Festival of Radical Drama, Dutch master of the theatrical
avant garde Koenraad Hooeblijnck makes his triumphant return to Agnes Porter
Theater with his newest work: a literal interpretation of Edvard Munch's famous
painting, The Scream (or "De Shreeuw," in Dutch). Hoeeblijnck's sustained, teeth-
rattling, primal howl will have you "shreeuwen" for more! (Each performance is one
full day long. One intermission. No snacks.)

A CHRISTMAS CAROL *November 25 to January 3*
Charles Dickens' holiday classic is back! Of course, it didn't *have* to be back. We
could've mixed it up this year—maybe with a straightforward *Romeo and Juliet*, or
even *Wicked*. Christ, we would even do *Wicked*. It's come to that. But no, everyone
wants *A Christmas Carol*, so, come to *A Christmas Carol*! Starring the Pawnee Players,
some local favorites, and in her Indiana theatrical premiere, *The Jersey Shore*'s Sammi
as Mr. Fezziwig!

I molded these boys into men, and then into Champions, and then into Swansons.

Hoosier Basketball Fundamentals

by Ron Swanson

In the great state of Indiana, there is no greater pursuit for a young shaver than to learn the fundamentals of the greatest American sport: basketball. If you want to play soccer, go to Greece. Every year, the most elite basketball players in the land of Indiana band together to pursue the greatest goal known to mankind: the defeat of Purdue.

The traditions of Indiana basketball have been handed down by our most revered forefathers and community heroes. But none has been more venerated than the High Priest of cagers, the man who more than any other represents Indiana basketball's beautiful tradition. I'm talking of course, about Gene Hackman.

Gene Hackman is best known for leading the Hickory Huskers to the 1952 Indiana State High School Championship in the 1986 movie *Hoosiers*. (Yes, it's just a movie, but it's the greatest goddamn movie of all-time, so shut your mouths and listen.) If you want to know everything you need to know about Indiana and basketball, just watch Gene Hackman in the movie *Hoosiers*. My only quibble with Gene Hackman in the movie *Hoosiers* is that at one point he says that if a player "plays to his potential, and is the best that he can be, then no matter what the scoreboard says, that player is a winner." This is the stupidest thing I have ever heard. If the scoreboard shows you have scored fewer points than your opponent, you are a loser. Mr. Hackman: you're a fine actor, but let's cut the crap and teach these kids what life is really all about. I also hate his policy of allowing his players to shoot free throws in the "Granny style." But I'll let that one pass.

When it comes to play selection, Gene Hackman has no rival. His offensive play the "Picket Fence" is literally indefensible and has never failed in history. He is also quite inspiring as a speaker. I am moved nearly to tears at the end of any game he coaches, and for me, "nearly to tears" is the equivalent of unbridled sobbing in most men.

The other legend of the game is Robert Montgomery "Bobby" Knight. Nicknamed "The General," Bobby Knight is 50 percent testosterone and 50 percent guts, a ratio I support fully.[45] Plus, he screams and curses constantly, which I wholeheartedly endorse. His panache is best exemplified by a locker-room speech he gave his Hoosiers during halftime of a game against Purdue in the 1980 NCAA Tournament: "If you don't play better, I will [*expletive*] the [*expletive*] out of you [*expletives*]. Those [*expletive*]-faced, [*expletive*]-sucking [*expletives*] that call themselves Boilermakers are nothing short of [*expletive*]-pissing, [*expletive*] [*expletive*]-[*expletive*] [*expletive*]-bags."

I met Coach Knight once, and told him I'd had great success in communicating my displeasure on the court by hucking a chair across the floor. Imagine my pride when The General followed my lead in a game against, once again, those godforsaken Boilermakers in 1985, and was proudly suspended for one game and placed on a two-year probation. In my opinion, it was his finest moment as a coach. (His second-greatest achievement was his assault on a police officer during the Pan Am Games of 1979. He was sentenced to six months in jail, but Puerto Rico couldn't extradite him out of Indiana. He was too much man. Nice try, Puerto Rico.)

Here follows my recommended course of discipline through which a young man can develop his skills in both the offensive and defensive arts, until he achieves a level of prowess that earns him the right to be called: "Hoosier."

OFFENSE

DRIBBLING Practice dribbling on a gravel driveway, left-handed, with a blindfold on, while your friend tries to elbow you in the groin. Can't do it? Quit basketball. This is a man's game.

---

[45] For more on things Ron supports fully, see Appendix 2: The Swanson Pyramid of Greatness.

PASSING Zero passes is selfish. One pass is American. Two passes is Communist. If your defender is "all over your jock," try passing the ball firmly to his face and see if he doesn't give you some breathing room.

SHOOTING Every morning, when you're done splitting firewood, shoot 100 free throws. If you make 90 or more of them, reward yourself with a hamburger. If you make 100, call me up and I'll come over and punch you in the face, because you're a liar. Steve Alford[46] couldn't make 100 in a row, and he was unquestionably the greatest shooter the world has ever seen at any level.[47] After you shoot 100 free throws, shoot 100 layups from each side of the basket. If you make 95, eat a hamburger. Then shoot 100 3-pointers from every spot outside the arc. Then eat a hamburger, no matter how you did. You need your strength.

REBOUNDING If you can't shoot, offensive rebounding is an arena in which the clumsier lads can shine. Basically, you just want to get between the defender and the basket, and shove him away with your backside. The thicker and stronger the backside, the better. Glad you ate all those hamburgers, aren't you?

DEFENSE

MAN-TO-MAN Keep your knees bent and focus on your man's navel. He can fool you with his knees and elbows, but the belly tells no tales. Don't be afraid to "get all over his jock," but beware of a chest pass to your face. If you cultivate a powerful body odor, it can really screw up a shooter's concentration.

ZONE Don't *ever* play zone defense. Zone is a particularly Michigan-flavored style of weakness.

STEAL Your hands should be fast as lightning. Practice catching mosquitoes with your bare hands until the entire insect world fears you.

REBOUND Listen to me very carefully. There is no excuse for not being a good rebounder. You just have to want it. Do whatever you have to do to grab that rock. Nothing is off-limits. *Nothing.* It also helps if you are tall.

MIND GAMES Mark your territory by emptying a nostril onto your opponent's jersey "accidentally." He'll think twice before returning to your zone.

---

[46] Steve Alford, b. 1964, was a member of the 1987 Indiana Hoosiers National Championship basketball team.
[47] No, he was certainly not.

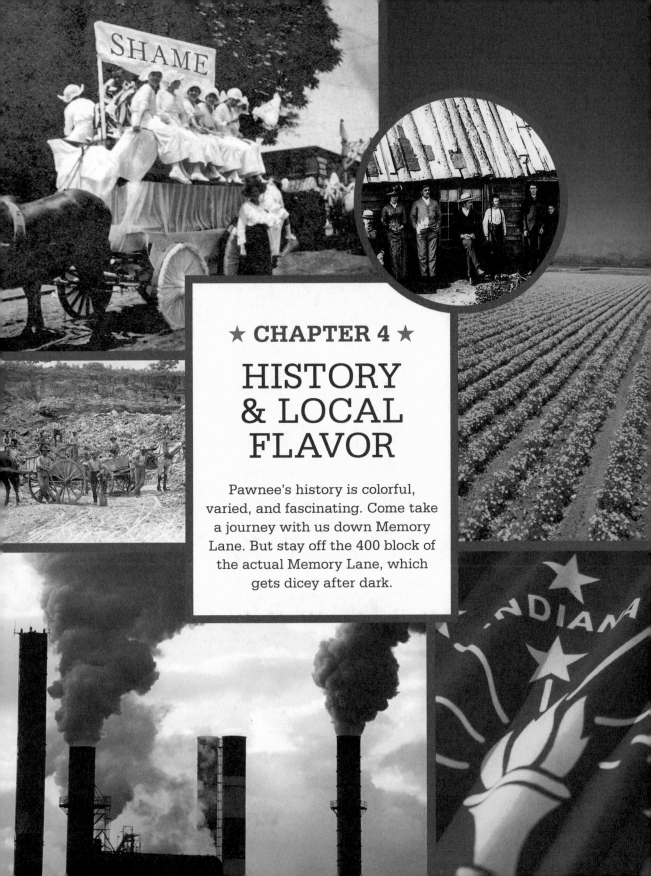

★ CHAPTER 4 ★

HISTORY
& LOCAL
FLAVOR

Pawnee's history is colorful,
varied, and fascinating. Come take
a journey with us down Memory
Lane. But stay off the 400 block of
the actual Memory Lane, which
gets dicey after dark.

4

The Birth of Our Town: The Story of Reverend Luther Howell and the Founding of Pawnee

Part I: The Man from the East

Luther Norton Howell was born in 1779 in Rehoboth, Massachusetts. He grew up to be strong of body and mediocre-to-degenerate of character. As a young man, he left the family business (harpoon sharpening) to try his luck at petty larceny, booze, whoring, and organizing dog, cock, bear, goat, and village idiot fights throughout southern New England.

In 1814, he joined a group of early pioneers on a journey west. Some of these bold Americans were drawn by the romance of wide-open spaces. For others it was the promise of fertile Midwestern soil. For Howell, it was several dozen death threats that had piled up after years of petty larceny, inveterate gambling, cuckolding, and running a crooked dog/cock/bear/goat/village idiot fight[48] in Hockanum, Connecticut. It was on this journey west, to the newly established community of Terre Haute, that Howell met and married his first wife, Ida. She was beautiful, hardworking, and twelve.

Of course, every Pawnee schoolchild knows what happened next . . . or do they? (Spoiler alert: they do not.)

The story goes that somewhere along the hard road to Terre Haute, Luther Howell found religion, leaving his sinning ways behind and becoming ordained as a Lutheran minister. Then finding the largely Catholic Terre Haute unfriendly to his Lutheranism, Howell set out to find a place where men and women could worship as they please. He

---

[48] Yes, all fought at once. Weirdly, the goat usually won.

came upon a lovely spot in Southwest Indiana and founded both the community that would come to be known as Pawnee, as well as its first Lutheran Church.

But that story isn't entirely true. Or even partially true, really. Turns out that Howell was *driven* out of town after sleeping with seven different men's wives, marrying four additional twelve-year-olds, running a prohibited dog/cock/badger/deer/buffalo/possum/skunk/village idiot fighting ring, and "refusing to wear breeches on the Sabbath and most Thursdays." Further, the Reverend Luther Howell wasn't so much a "Lutheran" minister, based on the teachings of Martin Luther, but a "Lutheran" minister, based on the random, self-serving, and morally bankrupt teachings of himself, the Reverend Luther Howell. So when Howell claimed he was leaving Terre Haute because he was being persecuted for his religion, the religion he referred to was one based on polygamous child-marriage, ritual animal sacrifice, pantslessness, and something Howell called "dong worship."[49]

Having had enough of his miserable corruption, an angry mob arrived at Howell's door, only to find that the reverend had left them a note: "Heading west to enjoy the untold promise beyond the mighty Mississippi. Please forward any correspondence or eligible twelve-year-old girls to the address below." Seventeen days later, after misreading his compass, an exhausted and badly wind-chapped Howell found himself about seventy miles[50] southeast, planting his personal flag on a pleasant patch of prairie,[51] and establishing a new city by uttering his famous declaration: "This seems good enough."

In honor of this event, every May 14 Pawnee celebrates Howell's arrival with our Founder's Day. Every April 27, Terre Haute celebrates Howell's exodus with their Departure of the Monster Day.

Part II: Enter the Wamapoke

Of course, Luther Howell wasn't the first person to think that Pawnee was an awesome place to live. A Native American tribe called the Wamapoke had lived

---

[49] On the plus side, Howell may have been the first person ever to use the word "dong" to refer to the male sex organ. It's hard to tell for sure—*The Oxford English Dictionary* is a little hazy on the etymology. I guess it's not a super-huge bonus if he was indeed the first person to use "dong," but he doesn't have a lot to hang on to, Howell doesn't, so I'm going to give this one to him.

[50] Howell's journey is often called the "Hundred-Mile Exodus," and indeed, he did walk almost one hundred miles, but he was so bad at navigation that he zigzagged all over the place and only ended up about seventy miles away from Terre Haute.

[51] This spot is commemorated by a plaque located in the alley behind the P.C.B.Y. ("Pawnee's Best Yogurt." The "C," they claim, is silent. Lame. But it's totally Pawnee's best yogurt.)

An Excerpt from the Diary of Reverend Luther Howell, Founder Of Pawnee[52]

April 27, 1817

Today I venture Westward from the comfortable bosom of my homeland, Terre Haute, Indiana, in search of that most basic of all American freedoms: the right to practice my religion. I can no longer stand the provincial attitudes and tyrannical customs of those I leave behind. I am an American and must be free to worship in my own way. I choose to do that by taking four wives and gambling heavily. Why is that so hard to get behind, I wonder? I started taking multiple wives four years ago and have been deliriously happy ever since. The Lord wishes us to have pleasure, and we must acquire this pleasure, through fraud if necessary. That seems so obvious to me. Anyone who doesn't get that is just being stubborn. We head West to California!

May 4, 1817

Our journey is hard, but the open expanses of the West beckon, and so we press on and face our challenges. My wife Ada is a wonderful cook and provides us with delicious meals. My wife Carrie is an expert seamstress and has mended two shirts that would have been otherwise destroyed when I fell into some bramble. My other two wives are Mary and Elizabeth, and I don't know them that well. They seem nice.

May 9, 1817

I fear that we may not have gone Westward. In fact, we may have gone Eastward, or perhaps Northward. Where are we? And what is this stench?

Mary has abandoned us. We got into a fight about how I was paying more attention to Elizabeth than to her. "I most certainly am not," I cried in my defense. "I don't even like Elizabeth that much—she's kind of mannish." This frankly didn't help matters, as it soon led to Elizabeth storming off in a huff. Thanks be to the Almighty God for Ada and Carrie, who provide me with the helpmeet comfort I need. Thanks be to the Almighty God also for Patricia, a new wife I picked up yesterday in an alehouse, who is kind of sullen but has legs up to here.[53]

May 10, 1817

Westward was our intent, but it appears Almighty God had a different plan for our expedition, for after walking for some 30 hours in a row, and coming upon the same exact cluster of trees four or five times, and after being under attack from Ada, Carrie, Patricia, and Laura (whom I met this morning) for what they claimed was a poor sense of direction, we have decided to stop our journey here. I have placed my flag in the ground and claimed this land as our new home. It seems good enough. In fact, it seems perfect. A new land, with new hope. Our town shall be a beacon upon a hill, shining forth with the promise of new beginnings, of a place where man can be free from persecution, and can fulfill his destiny as agents of the Almighty God, to live and prosper, evermore, Amen.

May 11, 1817

This place is awful. I hate it. I made a huge mistake coming here. Almighty God, why dost thou hate me so much?[54]

---

[52] Excerpted from "Westward the Course of the Hero Makes Its Way," by Rev. Luther Howell, first published posthumously in 1844. Reprinted 1966, University of Indiana Press, and here translated into normal English from that annoying old-timey English where the "s"s look like "f"s by Leslie Knope.

[53] In the original text, this passage is accompanied by a self-portrait of Howell holding his hand at eye level, perpendicular to the ground, presumably to indicate up-to-how-high his new wife Patricia's legs are. Your humble translator has decided against reproducing it here.

[54] The answer, by now, should be obvious.

here for at least two hundred years before he showed up. The Wamapoke were a proud people.[55] They wove beautiful and distinctive circular baskets. They grew corn.[56] They occasionally scalped their enemies.[57] They were also, in May of 1817, quite puzzled to learn that their settlement was suddenly sovereign Christian territory.

A small group of Wamapoke rode out to Reverend Howell's encampment, joined by a member of a group of French trappers with whom they had enjoyed a long and harmonious relationship. Using the trapper as an interpreter, the Wamapoke politely explained that they had lived there for several generations and would prefer that Howell not claim their land as his own. After pretending to listen intently for a while, Howell asked if they are members of the legendary Pawnee tribe he had heard about. They said no, they were Wamapoke. Howell famously replied: "You all look the same to me. How do you and the Pawnee tell each other apart? Anyway. I'm gonna go ahead and name this place Pawnee."[58] The Wamapoke decided that it wasn't worth the energy to correct him.

Part III: Exit the Wamapoke

Not long after Howell arrived, a group of Scandinavian immigrants appeared on the scene. They had been en route to Terre Haute when they heard its bigoted people had driven out a brave Lutheran minister simply for practicing his religion, so they'd called an audible and joined Reverend Howell's new settlement. Backed by his new congregation, Howell rode over to the Wamapoke settlement and asked *them* to leave. The Wamapoke politely refused, citing their hundreds-of-years head start on living in the area. They also suggested that the new settlers and the Wamapoke tribe could live in harmony, helping each other to live better on the unforgiving terrain of Southern Indiana. Howell pretended to listen and nod thoughtfully, then went back to his camp, got a bunch of guns, and returned to the Wamapoke settlement, asking them to make sure "they didn't let the wigwam door hit them on the ass on the way out."[59] Thus began decades of needless conflict between the Native Americans who reveled in the bounty of the open land, and the other people, who were annoyed at having to share.

---

[55] And still are. Pawnee is proud of the continuing contributions of our Wamapoke friends.

[56] And still do. Pawnee is proud of the continuing contributions of our Wamapoke friends.

[57] Our Wamapoke friends *do not* scalp anymore. Although tribe treasurer Marjorie Qualls does offer fine ladies' cuts and permanents at **From Hair to Epermity**, 290 Howell Drive, by appointment only.

[58] Of course, we do not know exactly what was said. This is how Howell's speech is presented in the annual "History of Pawnee" theatrical pageant performed by Mrs. Bergsson's tenth-grade history class at Pawnee Central High, which is as good a version as any to quote, I think.

[59] Possibly not a direct quote.

The Wamapoke experience in Pawnee has been mixed.

Howell was delighted to be free from the scourge of the polite and industrious natives. The settlers sat down to hear Reverend Howell's first sermon to his new congregation, and, expecting to hear the standard Lutheran invocation at the beginning of the service, they were surprised to see Howell begin instead with the "ritual removal of the breeches," as well as the subsequent "wagging of the dong." By sundown, Howell was on the run again. A year later he was killed in a dog/bear/cock/badger/wolverine fight in Kalamazoo, Michigan, when the animals finally wised up and joined forces against their common enemy.

No, Reverend Howell wasn't perfect. Okay, fine, he was a dick. But the town he founded overcame his thoughtlessness and corruption and has flourished in the two hundred years since he set off from Terre Haute with nothing but a dream, several thousand dollars of embezzled gold, and his child bride. If you would like to pay homage to Reverend Howell, his wolverine-gnawed bones are located in the University of Michigan (at Kalamazoo) Biology Department, where they were reassembled into a partial skeleton and used to teach college students about the medical condition known as "micropenis."[60]

[60] See Prof. Reginald E. Campopiano (Indiana State University), "Effects of Socially Embarrassing Male Sex Characteristics on Narcissistic and Amoral Behavior: How Reverend Luther Howell Gave Indiana the (Tiny) Shaft," *Indiana Journal of Unusual Medicine and Baseball Card Price Guide* (1989).

CITY OF PAWNEE
HISTORY OF WAMAPOKE
INCIDENTS

KEY ▮ = Terrible Things Happened

○ = Nothing Terrible Happened

1836 U.S. Cavalrymen approach a small Wamapoke settlement with the intention of burning it, realize that no one has a light, return to camp to get matches, take a wrong turn on way back to the settlement, and decide to just forget about the whole thing.

1882 From a distance, a myopic settler sees a Wamapoke man walking across a field. He waves, thinking it's his buddy Dave. Later, he runs into Dave at the saloon. Dave informs him of his error.

1860 After their participation in the Wamapoke Slaughter of 1859, a U.S. Cavalry unit comes upon a settlement and decides that they've been there, done that. They skip burning it down and head home for a nap.

1883 A group of white teenagers pass a group of Wamapoke teenagers and exchange hard looks, but that's pretty much it.

INDUSTRIAL MANUFACTURING ZONE

LINCOLN HEIGHTS

SCHUYLER PARK

MENOMINEE VILLAGE

CEMETERY

HWY 20

PAWNEE BOUNDARY

INDUSTRIAL MANUFACTURING ZONE

WASHINGTON SQUARE

REDEVELOPMENT AREA

HWY 34

SOU

HWY 231

CITY OF PAWNEE
STATE OF INDIANA

N
W E
S

CITY OF PAWNEE INDIANA 1817

1893 A white middle-school bully starts a fake rumor that one of the Wamapoke kids still wets the bed. Dick move? Sure. Atrocity? No!

1853 A wagon stacked with containers of liquid mercury bound for a silver mine in Colorado drives into a ditch. Large quantities of mercury pour into a watering hole used by several Wamapoke families and renders it unusable for decades. Horrible. But technically, not an atrocity.

1848 Hair-Like-Fire, favored daughter of Chief Wakote, meets a settler named Jedediah Smalls one evening as both arrive at a creek to water their horses. It is love at first sight. They kiss. News of their romance causes the Wamapoke Slaughter of 1848. But the kiss was nice.

The site of **Boring Rock**. Nothing ever happens at Boring Rock.

1868 U.S. Cavalrymen shoot three hundred buffalo for kicks. They have no bullets left when the Wamapoke arrive at the camp to complain.

PAWNEE BOUNDARY

HIGHLAND PARK

PAWNEE BOUNDARY

CO ROAD 20

TOWN

HWY 20

VONNEGUT HILL

DEVELOPMENT AREA

YBEND

Airport

CO ROAD 4

SCALE

1000   2000   3000   4000   5000

FEET

Our Wamapoke Friends

In today's Pawnee, members of the Wamapoke nation live side by side with the rest of us "settlers," living and working in most walks of life.[61] But why are there any Wamapoke here if Reverend Howell kicked them all out? Well, they lived in relative harmony and prosperity on the banks of Ohio's Olentangy River, but in 1831 President Andrew Jackson issued an order that forced the Wamapoke and numerous other tribes from their land. In one of history's great twists of fate, the Wamapoke found themselves relocated to a reservation . . . in Pawnee! This spurred Chief Mkwana'ami to utter the immortal phrase "Really? There's nowhere better?" which has been used on town tourism brochures for decades, with different punctuation.

As a proud Pawneean, I would like to say our ancestors welcomed the Wamapoke with open arms, but alas, it was a long, pothole-filled road from their shameful expulsion in 1817 to the glorious opening of the **Wamapoke Casino and Tax-Free Cigarette Emporium** (3000 Route 37) in 2005.[62] For those seeking a sobering examination of the atrocities committed against the Wamapoke, or who are looking to turn back the clock for some retro seventies fun, I highly recommend visiting the **Wamapoke Atrocities and *Welcome Back, Kotter* Collectibles Museum** (201 Walden Street), in the garage of tribe member Denny Willits. There are also several books and articles that document the many, many tragic events that took place here, in our otherwise wonderful town.[63]

---

[61] Interestingly, none of the dedicated volunteers who dress in traditional native garb at the **Indiana Living History Museum** (2240 Route 37, about five miles south of town) and weave baskets and stuff are actually Wamapoke, so be warned. You have no idea how hard I tried to get my money back.

[62] Do not take this supportive statement about the Wamapoke Casino as an endorsement of its advertising campaign, which disgustingly promotes the "Loosest Slots in Indiana." Yes, your author understands that "loose slots" refers to slot machines that supposedly win more frequently than other machines. No, your author will not "lighten up."

[63] See Clyde Monfreet, *Blood on the Plains: Native/Settler Conflict in Pawnee 1817–1880* (University of Indiana Press, 1990); Erwin Q. Stope, *Blood Everywhere: The Wamapoke in the 19th Century* (Vincennes University Press, 2001); Harper Struth, Sonja Pettermutter, and Hyrum Hewitt, eds., *You've Never Seen So Much Blood—Really, There Was Just a Phenomenal Amount of Blood: An Oral History of the Wamapoke Experience* (Prairie Wind Press, 1981); Dennis Rasmussen, "Even By American/Native American Standards, This Was a Horrible Way to Treat People," *American History Review*, May 1977; John L. Merginly, "Give Me One Good Reason Why Reverend Luther Howell Isn't Mentioned in the Same Breath as Idi Amin, Pol Pot, and Joseph Stalin When People Talk About Awful People," *Historical Ledger*, October 1993; Wendy Lonnergan, "Did the Settlers of Pawnee, Indiana, Ever Do One Even Marginally Not-Terrible Thing in Their Miserable, Disgusting Lives?", *Rearview Magazine*, January 1988; Denny Willits, *We Shall Not Be Torn Asunder: The Defiant History of the Wamapoke People and* Welcome Back, Kotter *Collectibles Price Guide*, self pub. (2007).

Why Do I Live in Pawnee?

An essay by Assistant City Manager Benjamin Wyatt

In the spring of 1999, I took a job with the State Government in Indianapolis as a budget specialist. That meant, essentially, that I reviewed, audited, organized, and slashed the failing budgets of towns and municipalities all over the state. Are you dead yet, from boredom? Did your organs shut down out of sheer apathy when you just read what my job was? I don't blame you. I would say it was the job equivalent of watching paint dry, but at least paint comes in many colors. All Indiana municipal budget-adjustment documents are the same shade of green, which I affectionately call "pale vomit."

There was one good thing about it, however: it afforded me the opportunity to live in a lot of different places—like Atlanta. Atlanta, Indiana, that is—a bustling metropolis of nearly 823 people, spread out over a third of one square mile in the middle of I'm sorry my organs just shut down from boredom while thinking about my time in Atlanta, Indiana.

After that I was assigned to Daleville, Indiana. Abraham Lincoln was raised on a farm near Daleville, and Florence Henderson was born there, and being both a history buff and a creepily knowledgeable fan of *The Brady Bunch*, I figured I could hack a six-week stay. Until I looked it up and realized that Lincoln and Henderson were actually from *Dale*, Indiana—not *Daleville*. Nobody is from Daleville. If you ask the cows in Daleville where they are from, they lie and say "Muncie," because saying you're from Daleville is just too sad and embarrassing. Sorry, America's Greatest President and 1970s TV's greatest mom/author of young Ben Wyatt's most vivid sexual fantasies—guess I'll see you some other time.

But my time in Daleville was a freaking hallucinogenic mushroom trip next to the nine weeks I spent in Muckland, Indiana, population *eight*, down in Harrison County on the Kentucky border. You wouldn't think a town with eight people and upwards of zero traffic lights could have a budget problem, but lo and behold, Mayor Steve Foppl had spent most of the town budget on archery targets, and it took me the better part of a month to sort out his excellent municipal budget filing system, which consisted mostly of writing down what he had bought, and for how much, with a Sharpie, on archery targets.

I lived in forty-six towns, in eleven years. Some tiny, some big . . . some suburban, some rural . . . some scenic, some that looked like film sets from *Blade Runner*.[64] But their differences were not the problem. Their problem was their essential *sameness*. Every one of them was 85 to 95 percent Caucasian. The median income was between $30,000 and $45,000. They all laid claim to some quirk of history ("We were the first town in America to use garbage disposals!"). Everyone told me that I *had* to go to [Whoever's] Diner, because it had *the best* cherry pie *in the entire world*, and that was not an opinion, mind you, it was an *honest-to-God fact* that had been somehow verified by professional scientists from the University of Food. And I might have been skeptical, but you know what? When I tasted that pie, I had to admit . . . *it was exactly as good as every other piece of cherry pie I had ever had*, including the one I'd eaten at [Whoever's] Diner in the last town I visited.

And then I got sent to Pawnee: 87 percent Caucasian. Median income $38,360. Birthplace of not-really-that-famous suffragette Dorothy Everton Smythe. And featuring JJ's Diner, home of the World's Best Waffles.[65] I settled in for what promised to be an exhilarating nine-week(!) stay.

Their budget was a mess—far worse than most I had dealt with, owing to the financial crisis, shrinking property tax rolls, and fiscal mismanagement from their city council that had to be seen to be believed. (A city councilman named Bill Dexhart had managed to write into the city code that the taxpayers were responsible for child support *and* birthday presents for his three illegitimate children.) I passed my time dreaming about Snerling, Indiana—my next assignment, where cows outnumber people forty to one and the general store's billboard off Route 256 proudly advertises that their toasters are big enough to toast "Jewish muffins," which I assume are bagels.

So why did I stay?

I suppose it all began when I met Leslie Knope, second in command of the Department of Parks and Recreation, and the most tireless crusader I have ever met in any government, or any profession, really. After we slashed her department's budget to a demoralizingly low, life-support level, she convinced her entire department to roll the dice on one big project—the Harvest Festival—which would either make enough of a profit to reinstate

---

[64] Note from Tom Haverford: What a nerd.

[65] I am very fond of Ben, but so help me God, if he says one bad thing about the waffles at JJ's Diner, I will end him.

her budget or fail miserably, in which case her department would be shut down entirely. She then personally worked about a hundred hours a week, for two months, doing nothing but making sure the festival would succeed. Which it did. Spectacularly.

It's hard to explain how much more impressive that was than every other decision made by every other government official I have ever met. The next-most noble thing I have ever personally witnessed was probably the time a city councilman in Valparaiso found someone's wallet on the floor and only stole $40 in cash before turning it in.

But it wasn't just Leslie. The people she works with turned out to be warm, kind, and thoughtful. Their gestures of friendship were not empty, as such gestures so often had been in other towns. The residents of Pawnee are grade-A weirdos, but they're weirdos who care—passionately, loudly, and sometimes unpleasantly intensely—but they care. Soon, Dorothy Everton Smythe's contributions to women's rights started to seem significant, and the waffles at JJ's started to seem like they just maybe *were* the best waffles in the world.[66] In short, I found myself thinking less about Snerling, or Atlanta, or Daleville, and more about how it was possible I had found a home.

So I stayed. And I haven't regretted it for one moment. Except the day I came home and there were three raccoons sitting in my living room, pooping on my couch and casually eating my iPad.

Anyway. If you have the time, you should come here. It's a nice place to live.

---

[66] You're goddamn right they are.

The Harvest Festival: Pawnee's Greatest Tradition

In November of 1938, local farmer Quentin Arble found himself with a massive pumpkin surplus. Not wanting the pumpkins to just rot in his field, he opened his farm to neighborhood kids, inviting them to pick as many pumpkins as they could carry and giving them free rides in a hay-filled trailer pulled by twenty of his strongest turkeys. Despite the many, many injuries and ensuing lawsuits, a Pawnee tradition had been born: the Harvest Festival.

For more than half a century, the Harvest Festival was one of Pawnee's most beloved institutions—a magnet for tourists from Southwest Indiana and beyond, who would come here to gaze in wonder at how fat our citizens were, and also to attend the Harvest Festival. From its humble beginnings, it blossomed into a weeklong event, featuring rides, attractions, food courts, animal exhibits, history tents . . . Pawnee actually had something to crow about! Until, tragically, in 1989, budget cuts and a particularly ill-timed and extremely public "Carny Streak"[67] caused it to be shut down.

Yes, the Festival generated revenue, but more importantly, it generated fantastic memories for generations of Pawneeans. I've been knocking on doors all over town asking people to share some of their favorites. For the most part, people were incredibly welcoming, but I don't care what that family at 227 Kirkwood Lane say, their perv dogs were not just saying "hi."

Without further ado, here are some of your Harvest Festival Memories, Pawnee!

"I was at the second Festival. I was fourteen. My cousin Bertram was in a farmer's collective— they were kind of Red—and they invited everyone in town to bring what they could. Vegetables, jarred preserves, eggs, what have you. Just neighbor helping neighbor. It was beautiful. Even

---

[67] Streaking was one of those things that Pawnee citizens kind of just quietly tolerated from the carnies who worked the Harvest Festival rides every year, but 1989 was the last straw. The carnies working the '89 festival did a bunch of crank, took off all their clothes, and ran screaming through the center of town right in the middle of the Pawnee Harvest "Breast"-ival Breast Cancer Awareness 5K Walk for the Cure. It was eleven o'clock in the morning.

those high hats from Eagleton came and shared stuff. Sack races, concerts every night—and it was all completely free! Right after it ended, some of the full-time strike-breakers from Sweetums took Bertram and his friends away. Next year it was 'The Pawnee Harvest Festival Brought to You by Sweetums.' Out with the socialist utopia, in with the corporate sponsorship. I didn't see Bertram for a full year, until the next year's festival, and he was working for Sweetums. He had a dead look in his eye. He wouldn't say where he had been or what had happened. Looked like a man who'd seen horrors I could only guess at. Dark things, that chewed up his soul and left him dry, inside-out, punched-through . . . a box with no lid, a chipped rock in search of its missing piece. But I won a pie at the Cake Walk, so that was neat."

—CLEM HARDAPPLE, NURSING HOME RESIDENT

"They used to have somethin' called Cracklin' Clouds. It was a kind of cotton candy machine that used pork fat 'stead of spun sugar. It was delicious. I still think about it every fall, when the air feels kinda like it used to round Harvest Festival time. Also when I write checks to that credit consolidation company what's helpin' me pay off my angioplasty."

—SHERM GOSS, PAWNEE POLICE CAPTAIN (RET.)

"I must've been, like, eleven. My mom took me to see the livestock exhibit and we saw a cow give birth! It was amazing. Just this perfect, tiny creature—one of God's miracles. It had a profound impact on me. I remember thinking: I want to eat that miracle."

—HEATH WONG, MR. WONG'S HAMBURGER SHACK

"When I was in sixth grade, Vice Principal Wieglund was in the dunk tank for charity. That vindictive, little, tyrannical, Napoleon-complex son-of-a-B must have raised $10,000 for the Kiwanis Club that day. God, we hated that man. I couldn't get a ball anywhere near the strike zone in Little League, but that day, my aim was true. One of the best afternoons of my life."

—WILL YELLE, GENERAL CONTRACTOR

"Favorite Harvest Festival memory? That's easy. 1981. John Cougar played. It was right before American Fool came out and he sang 'Jack & Diane,' looking at me the whole time. Afterwards, I lost my virginity behind the Skee-Ball machines to a guy saying he was John's manager, but who was actually just a skeevy guy who worked for the portable toilet company. Well, that skeevy guy and I have been married for twenty-nine years!"

—MOLLY SCHPRETZ, MEDICAL BILLING SPECIALIST

N

CITY OF PAWNEE, INDIANA
1817

Pawnee

Science Discovery

FARMERS FRUITS

FESTIVAL TENT

MUSIC CENTRAL

Racoon Pen

The Corn Maze

PPD
Emergency and Police Services

WAFFLE BOULEVARD

Bluegrass Stage

Tractor Tent

FERRIS WHEEL

DUNK TANK

HAYSTACK MOUNTAIN

HARVEST FESTIVAL HEADQUARTERS

SPAWNEE HANDWASH STATION

Hay Wagon

MILKING BARN

COWS OF OTHER STATES

COWS OF OUR STATE

Fortune Telling

WESTERN CIRCLE

Disco Dance Floor

Carnival Row

Picnic Area

CAROUSEL

HISTORY TENT

The Bunjee Jumper

KIDS PETTING ZOO

Picnic Area

Cow Rides

Cottoncadiverse

Taco Alley

"Fall of '79, my dad puts our old AMC Hornet station wagon out on the front lawn with a For Sale sign. $750 or best offer. That night, he goes to bowling league and me, Pudge, Jo Jo, Freebird, and Dennis take the Hornet to the Festival and enter it in the demo derby. I smashed that thing up something fierce. It was awesome. I had to work cleaning bathrooms at the SuperSuites every day after school for my whole senior year to pay my dad back, but it was totally worth it. I am forty-nine years old and I am technically still grounded."

— JIM CRAYBER, FORKLIFT OPERATOR

"It was 1958. Me and my brother Eddie entered as a hoot, but it turned out we had an honest-to-Pete gift! It's like we were put on this earth to Three-Legged-Race. We were unstoppable! We won every Harvest Festival from '58 until '62. Me and Eddie still talk about how that was the time in our lives when everything seemed possible. What memories! Then in '63 Eddie turned fifteen and aged-out, and then we both started drinking a lot."

—EARL HESHUM, INMATE

"That would be Harvest Festival '86. The one where that kid got his hand all ground up in the mechanism for the Ferris wheel. I was on that Ferris wheel. No! For real! I was sixteen and I went—man, I was such a dork then—I went with my mom and my sister. They wanted to go see the pig races, but I knew that the Arruda brothers had pigs competing and I hated those dudes. They used to pick on me. Body-check me into lockers and whatever. So, Mom and Jen go to the pig races and I'm up at the top of the Ferris wheel, just . . . brooding, plotting my escape from this lame-ass town, when the wheel just like, boom. Stops. Then I can hear the kid screaming. His mom's screaming. His dad is crying. People are panicking, running around asking if there's a doctor around. It was awful. This girl named Bonnie Flenck I think is in the car below me with her boyfriend and he has to, like, physically restrain her from jumping out. It was f'ing crazy. We were up there for more than two hours. And I was sitting up there by myself. Just hating everyone. Hating this town. And I looked out on the midway. Out toward Eagleton. I could see the high school. I could see Indian Tears Pond. Just . . . all of Pawnee, stretched out before me. And it was so beautiful. And I had never noticed before. I graduated a couple of years later, went off to Grinnell College in Iowa and had a blast and really found myself. When it came time to settle down and choose a home, I realized I wanted to move back here. It was the best decision I ever made."

—VERN BLANDSTEN, TEACHER

INDIANAPOLIS SUN

INDIANA'S HOMETOWN NEWSPAPER

Friday, October 27, 1989

LITTLE HORSE
IS BIG
DEAL!

LI'L SEBASTIAN

Pint - sized pony is breakout star of Pawnee Harvest Festival. Holds record for most photographed object in America for week.

32-PAGE SPECIAL SECTION WRAPS MAIN NEWS

The Triumphant Return of the Harvest Festival as Engineered by Leslie Knope with the Assistance of Individuals Too Numerous to Name in the Title of This Sidebar

He came back! (And soon after, he died, but still—he came back!)

Last year, the Harvest Festival made its triumphant return to our town, in a massive undertaking engineered by the Department of Parks and Recreation. More than eighty thousand paying visitors later, the previously stripped budget of our department had been restored, and we even had a budget surplus, which we almost lost because the comptroller's office thought it was a prank being played on them, but then we convinced them it was real and were able to use it.

The number one attraction, naturally, was Li'l Sebastian—miniature horse, local legend, and honorary PhD in Communications from Notre Dame University (1993).[68] Li'l Sebastian made his public debut at the Harvest Festival in 1989, and he was an instant sensation—his unique blend of cuteness and amazingness led to record-shattering T-shirt sales and something the *Indianapolis Star* called "Mini-Mania."[69][70]

His weeklong appearance at last year's Harvest Fest was, sadly, his last, as he passed away a couple months later, at the ripe old age of twenty-six. Thank you, Sebastian. You may have been li'l. But what you did for our town and my department was anything *but* li'l.

---

[68] In addition to this incredible honor, Sebastian was also the seventh-most-photographed object in Indiana during the time he was alive; he holds an honorary judgeship in Lafayette; he was honorary Poet-in-Residence at Ball State in 1991; his mane was once trimmed and the hair was used to make a pillow for Dan Quayle; he once appeared on stage with the band Warrant; and Alanis Morissette allegedly told a *Spin* magazine reporter that "You Oughta Know" was written about him.

[69] Note from Ben Wyatt: I just want to say that I still don't quite get what all the fuss is about regarding this small animal. So it's totally okay if you have no earthly idea why this horse was such a big deal.

[70] Note from Leslie Knope: No, it's not. It's not okay.

Interview with a Reasonableist

In 1974, a small religious movement called Reasonableism began in Pawnee. Though their beliefs—including the worship of a six-tentacled lizard god named Zorp with an erupting volcano for a mouth—were somewhat out of the ordinary, the Reasonableists rejected the term "cult," preferring the term "perfectly legitimate religion, I mean, look at the crazy things Buddhists believe, am I right?"[71]

Within months, Reasonableists had taken complete control of Pawnee, including all of its prominent government positions and the majority of its successful businesses. From 1974 to 1976, the official town slogan became "Engage with Zorp."

What follows is an interview conducted with Herb Scaifer, who was the Commodore's Messenger, or third in command, of Reasonableism. Herb is currently the proprietor of Herb's Spices and Herbs, a specialty food market in South Pawnee.

LESLIE KNOPE: Welcome, Herb, thank you for agreeing to this interview.

HERB SCAIFER: My pleasure. There's so much false information about Reasonableism and what it meant to Pawnee, I'm always happy to set the record straight.

LK: Let's start from the beginning. How did Reasonableism originate?

HS: Well, in 1974, a brilliant folder salesman named Lou Prozotovich wrote a self-help book called *Organize It!*[72] It was about clarifying and purifying your life through organization, mainly through the use of folders and various other organizational paraphernalia, but primarily folders.

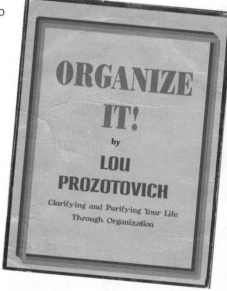

ORGANIZE IT!

by

LOU PROZOTOVICH

Clarifying and Purifying Your Life Through Organization

---

[71] Quote from "An Interview with Lou Prozotovich," *Pawnee Journal*, November 12, 1974. An interview worth reading on microfiche, if you can find it, if only for the fact that the author (Carl Wompert) begins the article extremely skeptical of Prozotovich and his new religion, and by the time the interview has ended, Wompert has fully converted to Reasonableism, and attained the level of Purveyor-VI, making him one of the more senior Reasonableists in town.

[72] © 1974 by Lou Prozotovich. *Organize It!* and all of its sequels and constituent and related books, pamphlets, tracts, folder-filing systems, medicinal recipes, spiritual guides, Zorp action figures, and courses for religious study and enlightenment are owned jointly by the Lou Prozotovich Estate and the plaintiffs and claimants of the landmark 1976 class-action lawsuit *Adherents of Reasonableism v. Prozotovich*.

LK: And this book became popular in Pawnee?

HS: Very popular. Topped the charts. It started being taught in schools. Most people had multiple copies. Z100 became a radio station that just looped an audio book recording of *Organize It!* Also, folder sales went way up, which was a nice, coincidental side benefit for Lou.

LK: Then what happened?

HS: Using his own system, Lou's life had become incredibly organized. He was probably the most organized person I've ever seen. He was so organized he had time to tutor hundreds of young women in one-on-one, private sessions, in the art of personal purification. And he decided to start talking about his system to larger groups.

     His skills were so great that he reached what he called "profound spiritual organization." "What if your spirit had folders?"—that was the question that really broke it open for Lou. I remember the first meeting of Reasonableism like it was yesterday. "We'll call it Reasonableism, because then if people criticize it they'll sound like they're criticizing something really reasonable," Lou said. He was right.

LK: So it became a successful religious movement right away?

HS: Not right away. The first meeting lasted about twenty minutes. Then it took another hour or so for word to spread in town. But yes, after that hour and twenty minutes, I would say most people in Pawnee were Reasonableists, give or take a few stubborn Baptists.

LK: What would you say were the basic beliefs of Reasonableism?

HS: Gosh, it's been a long time since I've thought about it—now I'm just a regular, everyday local business owner. As I remember, the basic beliefs were pretty typical stuff: the proper organization of mind, body, and spirit . . . the importance of hard work . . . and the birth of the planet in the belly of a giant space fish.

LK: I'm sorry, what was that last one?

HS: The importance of hard work?

LK: No. The—the fish one.

HS: Oh, right. [*Quickly.*] Earth was born in the belly of a giant space fish called Gog-44. Now, I wouldn't say that's one of the top one or two most important beliefs. It's probably third on the list. There's also another one about writing down your thoughts at the end of the day and putting them in a red folder. I probably should have said that one third, and then the Gog-44 one after that. I'm always forgetting that one.

LK: What can you tell me about Zorp?

HS: See, everyone always fixates on Zorp, but again, he wasn't really that big a part of Reasonableism.

LK: "Zorp. The Lizard God of Reasonableism. The Founder, the Power, the One True End-All, Be-All." I'm quoting from the sequel to *Organize It!*—*Organize It! 2: Engage with Zorp.*

HS: Well, sure, I'm not going to pretend Zorp wasn't a big deal. I mean, after all, he was an omnipotent twenty-eight-foot lizard. Hahahahahahaha. [*Laughter continues for several minutes.*] Look, here's the deal: Zorp is the creator of all things light, dark, material, and immaterial, born not of animal womb but forged in the icy cauldron of the galaxy's most foreboding folder-space, merciful, eternal, and capricious, long may he reign o'er the universe, spitting righteous fire from his mouth volcano. [*Pause.*] I'm sorry, what was the question?

LK: I'm not sure. What do you think caused the demise of Reasonableism in Pawnee?

HS: A variety of factors. Divisiveness, some petty jealousies between a few high-ranking members, plus also one day Lou left the country with 6 million dollars and nine pregnant women. And the many cat sacrifices led to some bad publicity.

LK: What do you say to accusations that Reasonableism was a cult?

HS: Is Hinduism a cult? Is Christianity a cult? Is Scientology a cult? What's the difference between something four hundred million people believe and something sixty thousand people and four hundred some odd cats believe? What is a cult, anyway? Was Abraham Lincoln a cult?

LK: . . . Am I supposed to answer that?

HS: The important thing is, Reasonableism, as harmless and really reasonable as it was, is completely over, and I am a regular, everyday local business owner with no outlandish beliefs and certainly no incentive to put mind-altering substances in the herbs and spices stocked at the mom-and-pop grocery store that I run.

LK: Okay. Well, thank you for sitting down with me, Herb.

HS: Thank you. Hey, if you have a second, I have some pamphlets I'd love you to read that discuss the many health benefits of yerba maté tea plus also they discuss Zorp.

LK: I'm good.

ORGANIZE IT! 2
ENGAGE WITH ZORP

LOU PROZOTOVICH

Reasonableism: The Basics

The following is excerpted from *Organize It!*, written by folder salesman Lou Prozotovich in 1974.

—CHAPTER FOUR—

The Next Level

Okay—if you completed Chapter Three, that means you have now designed your Personal Document Organization Method, you've bought plenty of folders, and you have adopted and embraced the Three-Pile System™. Remember—if a piece of paper can't fit into one of the Three Piles (Important Now, Important Later, Permanently Important), you don't need it!

Now that you have all your loose paper organized with the Three-Pile System™, we are ready to move on to the next level: organizing your life, with Reasonableism. "What's Reasonableism, Lou?" you ask. It's simple.

Reasonableism is a belief system that takes simple organizational techniques for filing papers, like the Three-Pile System™, and applies them to all facets of your life. Reasonableism enhances spirituality, builds lasting relationships to family, friends, and all life forms, and helps you maximize your targeted levels of personal achievement.

Reasonableism encourages its adherents to believe that anything is possible with the triumphant spirit of the human will, particularly when that will is augmented with a new and deep understanding of the actual (and heretofore unknown) origins of all life in the universe.

Reasonableism is more than the sum of several finite elemental truths, but there are some central tenets behind its philosophy. These include:

- Man is mortal in body but immortal in spirit.
- Man's abilities are profound and infinite.
- Man can use tools to unlock his unlimited potential; foremost amongst these tools is the folder.
- Zorp is the One True Lord; all must obey him or be destroyed in body and spirit.
- Filing old documents is the simplest way to unclutter your desk.

90

Reasonableism believes in the fundamental brotherhood of all life within the universe and in the essential goodness of mankind. Except for those who question the tenets of Reasonableism, or attempt to keep you from maximizing your potential by prohibiting you from employing the Three-Pile System™ or properly Engaging with Zorp. Those people are Unwanted Documents, who are cluttering up the filing cabinet of your life. We need to clean out that filing cabinet. Speak no longer to those people, hereafter referred to as "Clutterers."

Reasonableism is not an inflexible religion, but a living, breathing belief system with a benevolent leader (Zorp) who only occasionally demands attractive womanly sacrifices to his human emissary, Lou Prozotovich. Zorp appeared to Lou Prozotovich in the form of a wailing spirit-lizard and gave unto Lou Prozotovich a series of seventy ways to improve the temporally limited experience of human existence, the first of which was "Maintain a Clutter-Free Office Environment" and the seventieth of which was "Suck Down the Time-Shards of Parlaxx."

The other sixty-eight steps of Reasonableism are known only to Lou Prozotovich. That was just a taste.

Anyone who claims to have any knowledge of the other sixty-eight steps of Reasonableism, or anyone who discourages you from learning the other sixty-eight steps of Reasonableism, is a Clutterer, and we have already discussed what to do with Clutterers. You don't need their clutter! They belong in the wastebasket of your life. No more talking to them.

The overarching aim of Reasonableism is fundamental spiritual satisfaction using methods like the Three-Pile System™ and the Front Teeth Removal Plan™ and the Forty Sorrows of Zorp™ in order to reach a higher plane of enlightenment. Reaching this plane takes commitment, unquestioning dedication, and at the time of this writing, approximately $110,000. Zorp has directed Lou Prozotovich to accept personal checks.

Great work! You are well on your way. On to Chapter Five: "Color-Code Those Files, and Present Your Nude Groin for Zorp's Approval."

Haunted Pawnee

Does Pawnee have ghosts? Well, this town is so great, I'd want to hang around after I died, too! But are these just silly ghost stories or true horrifying accounts? You decide, guys and *ghouls*! Curl up in that *coffin* and continue reading this *book of spells*! If you dare! BOOOOOOOOOOOOOOOOOOOOO! SPOOKY THINGS!!!!

The House on Haunted Hill 29 Stonebridge Lane

The beautiful mansion at the end of Stonebridge Lane once belonged to Caleb Turner (1882–1949), one of the wealthiest men in town. Once a year, he would have an

extravagant dinner party and invite ten lucky guests from town. And every year, one of them would mysteriously disappear! The guests would then talk about how mysterious it was that yet another person had disappeared from Mr. Turner's fabulous dinner party. When Turner was asked about it, he would shrug and say, "I dunno. Maybe he got lost on the way home or something." Finally, the police were like, "Oh—Turner is killing those people." And they arrested him.

Scully's Bar 831 Nichols Lane

This bar was founded in 1892, and current bar owner Michael Scully swears that sometimes patrons from the 1800s still come in to grab a drink! (*Note: Scully has severe dementia due to eighty-plus years of continuous gin consumption.*)

Ray's Sandwiches 78 Primrose Street

Recently, I spoke with owner Ray Halstead, who swears his eatery has been haunted since it opened in 1985. "Legend has it," says Ray, "that a woman died of shock because of the 'spooky good deals,' and how 'scary good' the sandwiches were. She haunts the place to this day because she can't believe a twelve-inch meatball sub combo is only $4 and comes with chips and a free drink. So come to Ray's . . . if you dare! And if you want a great deal!" (*This is probably just Ray trying to get a free ad. But still—spooky.*)

RICKY'S ROCK-N'-ROLL BOWLING
3381 Route 9

Is there a spirit haunting lane seven at the Rock-N'-Roll Bowling alley? Well, the monitors flicker . . . the floor is mysteriously slippery in some areas . . . pins go missing . . . and the vending machine steals change! Also, this is the site of the 1978 Dorney family murders, where three people were axed in their brains.

The Lady from Eagleton

Drive down Kirby Lane late at night and you might just see a beautiful woman in a long white gown standing eerily on the side of the street. But don't pull over and pick her up . . . because she died twelve years ago! The story goes that she left her house in Eagleton and accidentally wandered into Pawnee, where she died of heartbreak after witnessing all the sorrow and shame and miserably ugly people. It is strongly believed this story originated in Eagleton, which would explain its offensive nature.

Don't Go to the Pawnee Cemetery after Midnight!

Because it is closed. A reminder from the Pawnee Cemetery Office.

The Library

The library is the spookiest place of all. Don't go there, or be cursed by the evil ugly witches who wear glasses without prescriptions to look smarter than they are. They all are terrible. Don't go there.

Donna Has a Ghost Story!

by Donna Meagle

Dictated to and Transcribed by Leslie Knope

It was February 21, 2008. The first and <u>last</u> time I let my stupid-ass brother borrow my Mercedes SUV. Here's how it happened. I'm outside the Cineplex waiting for LeVondrias to pick me up. The dude. Is. Always. Late. I had just seen *Definitely, Maybe* starring the both creatively and physically talented Mr. Ryan Reynolds. Suddenly, I hear a creepy-ass whisper in the wind, saying "Donna." I ask, *to the wind,* "Umm, and who the hell are you?" Silence. Two minutes later, more wind whispering, again with the "Donna." I am straight up about to *lose it.* Still no sign of LeVondrias, who is now *twenty minutes late.* So I call him and it goes straight to his rude voice-mail greeting. Hey, LeVondrias—here's an idea. Figure out a better way to present yourself to the world than just saying, "Leave a message." This. Is. Why. You. Do. Not. Have. A. Girlfriend.

I call him seven more times. Seven. And who do I hear from next? Lo and behold, the [*expletive deleted*] wind ghost. "Donna . . . Donna . . ." Finally, thirty minutes late, LeVondrias decides to pick me up. But hang on a second . . . what is that that I am seeing? *Oh. I'm sorry. Is that a ding on my 2005 Mercedes SUV bumper? Did you think that I would not notice? I noticed that [expletive deleted] before the car turned the corner. I could see that from a mile away in the dark. And you're gonna look into my eyes and try and tell me that was already there? LeVondrias, get your walking shoes on because you will never be inside my ride again. And don't walk in the street because I will run you down.*

I don't know what the ghost was.

Get to Know a Neighborhood: BRIDGEWATER COVE

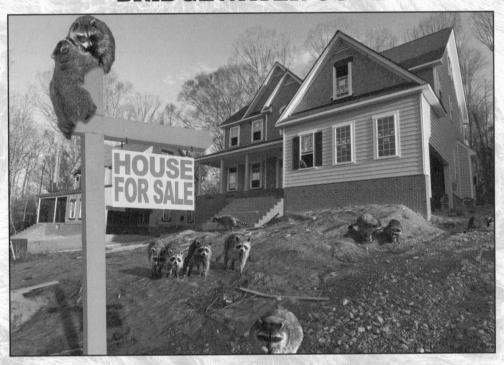

The Bridgewater Cove Development now houses several thousand of our masked friends.

In 2006, at the height of the housing boom, developer **Tom Norton** (owner and CEO of Norton Construction) built a large gated community he called Bridgewater Cove, despite there being no bridges, water, or coves anywhere in sight. The houses averaged $350,000, a massive sum for our town, and sold out in three weeks. Within a year, nearly every single one was **abandoned**. The area has mostly been ceded to animals, who

She's old, but she's dangerous.

have turned it into essentially a **massive raccoon shantytown**.

Some people still live in Bridgewater Cove, including the celebrated **Tilda Bird**, great-aunt of former Indiana Pacers basketball legend Larry Bird, who resides at 462 Indian Hill Road. Take a picture in front of her home! But *do not* enter it. Despite her frail appearance, Tilda knows her way around a **telescopic baton**.

Pawnee in 2116
by Chris Traeger[73]

First of all, let me just say that this book is literally one of the greatest ideas anyone has ever had on Earth. When Leslie told me she was compiling a book about Pawnee, I was excited, I was thrilled, I was delighted, and I was overwhelmed. I thought to myself: "This is going to be fantastic." Then she asked me to write something for it, and I literally have never been happier. I said I would be delighted to participate in any way I could. I offered up several ideas, including an Excel spreadsheet of all of my exercise routines, and the PowerPoint slides from my proposal to make Pawnee the home of an annual event I'm calling the Pawnee 1000 Hyper-Marathon, which would be one thousand people attempting to run one thousand miles in one thousand hours. She thought all of these ideas were fantastic, but I could tell she was not entirely enthused. I believe it is very important to be able to read people, and I take pride in my ability to be empathetic and understand what other people are feeling. This is a very important skill. Another important skill is listening. Also: generosity. "Generous people are the ones who pave the way for others to flourish." You know who said that? Me, Chris Traeger, in my high school valedictory address . . .

[section deleted][74]

. . . which is why I have never once used a soft-bristle toothbrush.

In any case, I then told Leslie that I would be also interested in writing some historical pieces, and that definitely piqued her interest. I explained that my own love of history comes from my desire to better understand how life changes over vast stretches of time. This topic interests me because I plan to be the first human being to live to be 150 years old. Leslie then came up with an idea that literally knocked me off my feet. It was by far—and I am deadly serious here—the most brilliant idea I had ever heard in my entire

---

[73] Leslie here. Quick editor's note: Chris's original essay was unreadable. It's not that it was poorly written—it was actually really good. But EVERY other WORD was in ALL CAPS and it made my eyes cross, a little. When I said, "Chris, I'm worried that people will feel like they're being yelled at," he replied, "But Leslie, I live my life in all caps." Which was weirdly endearing, but not persuasive. So, in the interest of readability, I removed all of the capitalized words. If you want to get the effect of his original text, just have your most upbeat relative read it to you REALLY LOUDLY.

[74] Leslie again. Chris is . . . enthusiastic, as a person and as a writer, and at times during this essay he got a little off-topic and began to just type things he thought or felt about the world, which perhaps were not 100 percent relevant to the issue at hand. When appropriate, I have just deleted those sections and noted their absence.

2011   *2040*

life. When I was fifteen a friend of mine had the idea for a bookstore you could access by computer, but this idea of Leslie's was in a way even better. I once had an idea I thought was fantastic, for a kind of breathalyzer device, but instead of alcohol it measured your food for saturated fat content . . .

[section deleted]

. . . a kind of cell phone that animals could use, but they refused to invest.

In any case, Leslie's idea was that I should write an essay wherein I look back, from my deathbed, on all of the changes I have seen transpire in Pawnee in my 106 years of living here. Fantastic, right? I thought so, too. I thought "fantastic!" and I also thought "so inventive!" and then I thought . . .

[very large section deleted]

. . . size 28 waist, even though no one believes me. Anyway, without further ado, here is 150-year-old Future Chris Traeger, reflecting on a life in Pawnee:

My Thoughts at 150

What a ride! I am so moved that so many of my friends, children, grandchildren, great-grandchildren, great-great-grandchildren, and my first great-great-great-grandson, Chris Traeger XIII, could be here at my bedside on the day my Total Body System Awareness Machine, which I first invented in 2019, tells me will be the day of my death. Each and every one of you has meant so much to me—especially my fifth wife, Xiu-Yi, who so sweetly helped me achieve my goal of mixing my genetic material with that of one woman from each of the inhabitable continents.

We have experienced so much together. But no one, of course, has experienced as much as I have, since I am 150. Looking out my window from the incredible comfort of my hoverbed, I see a city that few of my old friends at Pawnee City Hall could have imagined back in 2011. It is too bad that they all died decades and decades ago because they ignored my extensive diet and exercise advice. For example, not one of them listened to me when I told them to do more tricep workouts . . .

[section deleted]

. . . fold it over, then fold the other side, gently pull out the flap at the top, and voilà—a perfect origami sailboat!

If those friends of mine had lived, by the way, they would see a community transformed. They would see the seventy-five-foot-tall stalks of genetically modified HealthCorn that have helped make Pawnee the corn basket of the world. They would see the massive system of PeopleMover Treadmills that replaced the monorail back in 2090, which allow for both (a) rapid transport of people, if you walk in the direction they are moving, and (b) free and exhilarating exercise if you run in the opposite direction. The PeopleMover Treadmill System is based on a series of dynamic PowerPoint presentations I first made in 2015, which made most of the incredible things we see here today, from my window at Pawnee Super-Hospital Number 6, possible.

They would see the crystal-clear waters of the Pawnee River, reclaimed after a century of dumping from the Sweetums plant and rerouted to create a scenic river walk, along which hundreds of thousands of health-minded international tourists stroll as the river flows through wind-powered downtown, past the 100 percent green city hall, past the architectural wonder that is the compost-powered Pawnee Opera House, past the 100,000-seat all-solar-powered Traeger Field, home to the Pawnee Pioneers, three time National Super Rocket Ball League champions, and finally, past the statue that was erected in 2028 to commemorate my famous PowerPoint presentation of 2015 that laid the groundwork for these incredible achievements.

So, now, as my Total Body System Awareness Machine tells me I have only a few moments left on this Earth, I have no regrets. Except that I lied to all of you, because

2065   *2093*   *2116*

GOTCHA!⁷⁵ I am not dying! I modified the readout on the Total Body System Awareness Machine to make you all *think* I was dying, but it turns out that if you live to be 150, your body starts to regenerate—which I always suspected but never dared to express publicly for fear of being thought a madman—and I right now, at this moment, feel as good as I did when I was thirty! In fact—watch this!

(I now stand up and instantly run a 10,000-mile MegaThon, which takes me from Pawnee to the California coast and then back and then back again to California and then back again and then back to California, where I suppose I would need to be picked up . . .

[section deleted]

. . . lift a locomotive above my head like it was nothing, and everyone is shocked!)

The point, friends and family members, is that I will live another 150 years, and I plan to do so right here in Pawnee, Indiana—the greatest city in the world. And I hope you all join me. Especially my amazing children—you, Luo-Tong Traeger, and you, Nkote Agbonija Traeger, and you, Esperanza Lopez Traeger, and you, Dagbjört Hafthorsson Traeger . . .

[section deleted]

. . . the endless, inky-black void of death, which of course is just unacceptable.

See you all in 2266!

---

⁷⁵ This is the one time I felt it best to leave the word in all caps. It just makes stylistic sense.

The Miss Pawnee Pageant

One of Pawnee's grandest traditions is the Miss Pawnee Beauty Pageant, where a young woman is chosen to represent our great town based on her intelligence, substance, and integrity. In an ideal world. Usually, the hottest one wins.

I contacted Miss Pawnee 2009, Trish Ianetta, and asked her to write an essay entitled "What Pawnee Means to Me." She wrote back: "town." I asked her to elaborate. She then kindly sent this essay in the form of a series of Facebook wall posts. (I have annotated it with footnotes, where helpful.)

What Pawnee Means to Me

An essay about Pawnee, from 2009 Miss Pawnee Beauty
Pageant Award-Winner, Trish Ianetta

Trish Ianetta

Hi y'all. I don't even know where to begin talking about this awesome town that was founded over four hundred years ago![76] I am so beyond honored and hombled[77] to be asked by the mayor[78] to write this essay!

at 11:20 • Like • Comment

Trish Ianetta

Pawnee is so full of awesome stuff. We have stores and a McDonalds.[79] I mean just off the top of my head, I'd tell ya to check out our movie theater or go on over to the Pawnee Zoo and feed the animals.[80] Maybe take one of the bikes they have on the racks and ride them home.[81] There's so much fun stuff to do in Pawnee it's nutz.[82]

at 11:21 • Like • Comment

Trish Ianetta

Can I get deep with y'all?[83] [84] Pawnee's a special place you guys. You can do ANYTHING you make your mindset of. I was once just a local girl whose only real

---

[76] Pawnee founded in 1817.

[77] Not a word.

[78] Mayor Gunderson is not aware of Miss Ianetta's essay.

[79] See every other page of this entire book for listings of other local restaurants and businesses and points of interest. And for the record, we have three McDonald'ses.

[80] Please do not feed the animals.

[81] This would be theft. Pawnee currently has no bicycle exchange program.

[82] [sic]

[83] Unlikely.

[84] Sorry. That was mean.

101

goal was to get on YouTube. And would you believe that after just one month of winning Miss Pawnee, I was engaged to be *married?*! His name is Peter and he's so cute and fifty-eight years old. It's like Barbara Bush used to say, "The prettiness of their dreams is what happens to make life awesome."[85]

at 11:22 • Like • Comment

Trish Ianetta

When I was elected[86] by the town[87] to be your leader,[88] I promised to speak up for this values of a town.[89] I personally as though feel like if everyone just knew per se what their values were once for, then we could find that entitlement to treat one another and itself and not in vain or anything like that in Asia.[90] There is just a way that we can have fun, but and such as the birthing rate of immigrants is scary, so don't I feel as though the Middle East should have a tall wall around it so it becomes peace.[91] And that's what Pawnee means to me.

at 11:23 • Like • Comment

Trish Ianetta

Peace, love, and posper.[92]
Smoochies,
Trish

at 11:24 • Like • Comment

---

[85] Unclear what quote she is referencing here. Eleanor Roosevelt once said, "The future belongs to those who believe in the beauty of their dreams." The chances of Ms. Ianetta referencing Eleanor Roosevelt are zilch-point-bupkis. A quick Google search turns up nothing remotely close to this quote at all, and certainly not from Barbara Bush. I am going to assume that Trish (a) made it up entirely, or (b) a friend of hers named Barbara said it, or (c) she is drunk.

[86] Voted.

[87] Four judges.

[88] Pageant Queen.

[89] Not required or encouraged.

[90] I did not vote for Ms. Ianetta. It has become important to me that you all know that.

[91] I voted for a very intelligent, self-possessed woman named Susan Gleever, who played the piano and volunteered at a children's hospital.

[92] Sure.

Miss Pawnee Talent Competition Winners Through The Years

Year	Winner	Talent
1927	Margaret Swoope	Churning (Butter)
1928	Gladys Hendrickson	Churning (Butter)
1929	Gladys Berwick	Churning (Butter)
1930	Gladys Jensen	Churning (Butter)
1931	Frances Swoope	Churning (Butter, Curd)[93]
1932	Jane Hansen	Answering a Telephone
1933	Mary Glenden	Remaining Silent
1934	Gladys Floam	Spelling[94]
1935	Imogene Sysscroppe	Yelling Through Megaphone
1936 (a)	Edna Grable[95]	No Discernible Talent Demonstrated
1936 (b)	Luanne Parsons	Eyelash Batting
1936 (c)	Betty Hammersmith	Boobs
1936 (d)	Mary Hedges	Bach's Cello Suite No. 3 in C-major
1937	Stella Sackett	Charleston[96]
1938	Bronwyn Goethe-Braun	German Patriotic Demonstration[97]
1939	Barbara Swoope[98]	German Cooking Demonstration
1940	Edna Swoope (née Bly)[99]	Poetry Recitation (Endurance Category)[100]
1941	Maria Russo-Ishikawa	Italian and Japanese Patriotic Demonstrations
1942	Gladys Cartwright	Speech Opposing Retaliation for Pearl Harbor Attack

[93] Frances Swoope joins 1927 winner Margaret as the first sisters to win Miss Pawnee, in part by adding "curd" to her dynamic churning display.

[94] Ms. Floam was a born winner. She took the Blue Ribbon of Lady Achievement in the inaugural Harvest Day Ladies' Spelling Bee in 1938, winning on the final word: "What." Despite the Abbott and Costello–like hilarity that ensued after the sixteen-year-old Floam asked, "What is the final word?" the whole enterprise was a stain on both the Women's Suffrage Movement and the Pawnee educational system.

[95] 1936 was an all-around embarrassment. The crown was eventually given to fourth-place finisher Mary Hedges, after the winner and runners-up 1 and 2 were discovered exchanging sexual favors for the vote of Crawford Paxton, a judge for both the Miss Pawnee Pageant and the Seventh Circuit Court of Appeals.

[96] Pawnee has always been woefully behind the times in terms of dance trends, as evidenced by the spike in hospital admissions due to Twist-related injuries in 1978, and by Mayor Gunderon's Running Man–driven victory in the 2006 Mayoral Debate/Dance-Off.

[97] The great majority of Pawnee citizens around the start of the Second World War were not by any means Nazi sympathizers. They hated Hitler and everything he stood for, and many served valiantly in the armed forces. Some, however, were tremendous cowards, and pessimists, and began preparing for a world run by Germans the second they found out such a world was possible. (See Page 6; "Town Slogans Through the Years.")

[98] Daughter of Margaret. First mother-daughter Miss Pawnees.

[99] Second mother-daughter Miss Pawnee, though this one is iffy. The orphan Edna Bly was legally adopted by Margaret Swoope literally moments before victory.

[100] Recited Emily Dickinson's "A Drop Fell on the Apple Tree" 1,083 times in a row. Third most in Miss Pawnee history.

Year	Winner	Talent
1943	Barbara Bergen	Speech in Favor of Retaliation for Gladys Cartwright Speech
1944	NO PAGEANT*	*Wartime Sash Shortage
1945	Jane Roberts	Keeping Home Fires Burning
1946	Helen Trammler	Graciously Ceding Deeply Gratifying Job to Returning G.I.
1947	NO PAGEANT*	*Postwar Sash Shortage
1948	Isabelle St. Pierre	French Accent (Real)
1949	Kristin Christiansen	French Accent (Fake)
1950	Mary-Jo Mueller	Churning (Butter)[101]
1951	Lila Grint-Huber	Spotting Reds
1952	Frances Epperson	Spotting Reds
1953	Florence Swoope	Spotting Reds
1954	Marian Bernard	Naming Names
1955	NO PAGEANT*	*Anti-Communist Purge
1956	Grace Cranston	Lindy Hop
1957	Belinda Harvick	Getting a Good TV Signal
1958	NO PAGEANT*	*Slipped Organizer's Mind
1959	June Pigeon	Childbearing
1960	Phyllis Warner	Vaguely Offensive Impression of President-elect Kennedy
1961	Betty-Lynn Parker	Passing Resemblance to First Lady
1962	Mona Harper	Spot-on Impression of Secretary of State Dean Rusk
1963	NO PAGEANT*	*Mourning President Kennedy
1964	NO PAGEANT*	*Mourning President Kennedy
1965	NO PAGEANT*	*Curfew Imposed. Preparing for rumored "British Invasion."
1966	Lana Wallace	Pat Boone Medley
1967	Shelly Parker-Blanskin	Patriotic Songs
1968	Holly Flame[102]	"Full Frontal"
1969	Linda Morin	Tap Dancing
1970	Florence Butterworth	Tap Dancing
1971	Brenda Vincennes	Tap Dancing
1972	Marla Mundt	Tap Dancing
1973	Stacy-Ann Swoope	Tap Dancing
1974	Sandy Robinow	Tap Dancing
1975	Connie Hewes	Tap Dancing
1976	Deborah Swoope	Tap Dancing (Patriotic)
1977	Kelly Burkhardt	Tap Dancing
1978	NO PAGEANT*	*Anti–Tap Dancing Contingent Gets Pageant Canceled
1979	Hannah Bjornsen	Jimmy Carter Jokes

[101] Part of an unfortunate "The Men Are Back, Let's Be Women" postwar cultural regression.

[102] After Flame's performance, which she had perfected at the now-thankfully-defunct Wanna-poke Night Spot, Miss Pawnee's talent competition rules changed dramatically.

Year	Winner	Talent
1980	Kim Swoope[103] (née Hayes)	Piano
1981	Susan Andersen	Juggling (Balls)
1982	Roberta Fudge	Juggling (Bowling Pins)
1983	Lucy Chester	Juggling (Bowling Balls)
1984	Glenda Gamst	Juggling (Chainsaws)[104]
1985	NO PAGEANT*	*Mourning Glenda Gamst
1986	Debbie Wampeter	Disco Dancing[105]
1987	Peggy Snowden	Tying a Cherry Stem with Tongue
1988	Chelsea Bulpa	Wet T-shirt[106]
1989	Jennifer Swoope	Tap Dancing
1990	Jennifer Finch	Popping
1991	Deborah Slater	Locking
1992	Jessica Wicks	Popping and Locking
1993	Jessica Wicks	Weather Prediction
1994	Jessica Wicks	Packing a Suitcase
1995	Ashley Breidemeier	Flute (Ian Anderson's Solo on Jethro Tull's "Aqualung")
1996	Candace Yarbrough	Birdcalls
1997	Kelly Burleson	Fade-Away Jumper
1998	Laurie Dingley	Je Ne Sais Quoi
1999	Carrie Upson	Explaining Y2K Bug to Elders
2000	NO PAGEANT*	*Y2K Computer Meltdown[107]
2001	Unknown	Unknown[108]
2002	Amy Bradley	Speech Advocating Invasion of "Arabia"
2003	Shayne Pedersen	Patriotic Song
2004	Priscilla Andrews	Trash-Talk
2005	Vicky Ng	Interesting-Looking Skin
2006	Casey Vwitwick	Recited Plot of The Pelican Brief From Memory
2007	Amanda Milfred	Pole Dancing (Tasteful)
2008	Shannon O'Neil	Triple Jump
2009	Trish Ianetta	Boomin'[109]
2010	Amber Broxton	Getting Low

[103] First African-American Miss Pawnee. Second borderline-illegal adoption by dynastic Swoope family.

[104] Award presented posthumously.

[105] See Footnote 96, *supra*.

[106] Bulpa had found a loophole in the now-more-stringent Pageant Competition Propriety Guidelines, and they again had to be revised after her victory.

[107] Obviously, the threat of a Y2K "Meltdown" turned out to be a lot of hype. But it did affect Pawnee, when Mayor Gunderson panicked on New Year's Eve and ordered all the computers in the town to be melted down.

[108] Pageant held on September 10. Things got a little bananas around Pawnee after that, and the details of the pageant were instantly lost to history.

[109] This is the proper term for her talent, according to Miss Pawnee judge Tom Haverford.

Weird and Wacky Medical Stories from Pawnee St. Joseph's Medical Center

by Ann Perkins

Here's how this went down: Leslie asked me to contribute to this book. I suggested writing about my favorite Pawnee nature hikes, or the best bike trails. She stared at me, smiling blankly and nodding. Then I suggested something like "My Favorite Places in Town," and she just kept nodding and smiling. Then I finally figured out what she was after: freaky injuries.

Leslie *loves* hearing about freaky injuries.[110] And I've been a nurse in Pawnee for over ten years now, and there are some odd people in this town, so I've seen a lot of goofy stuff. So, because she's my best friend and I love her, here, Leslie (and whoever else is reading this), are the top ten weirdest things I've ever seen at Pawnee St. Joseph's Medical Center. (Everyone in these stories lived, so it's okay to enjoy hearing about their dumb injuries.)

1. We had a middle-aged couple who got drunk and passed out in the sun. And they were laying in a kiddy pool that had about an inch of water in it. It was a record day heat-wise and the kiddy pool actually melted around them like kind of a blue taco shell. Their son brought them in in the back of his Schwan's Frozen Foods truck.

2. This guy came in who had a scrunchie wrapped four or five times really tight around his penis. The really creepy thing was that it was his stepmom's scrunchie. And we know that because he kept telling us, like, over and over again: "This hair thing is my stepmom's! This hair thing is my stepmom's!"

3. There was a husband and wife who came in and they'd been keeping raccoons as pets. They told us that "after some toddies" they decided they wanted to make their raccoons go on the trampoline. I guess when they started jumping, the raccoons just went ballistic. There were lots of abrasions on the woman, and then when her husband—who'd managed to get off of the trampoline—started laughing, she hit him over the head with a broken-off mini-fridge door.

4. This one man got caught in the back room of a mall furniture store in Eagleton and he had shoved, like, a whole bunch of Christmas decorations up his butt. A teeny glass

[110] I really do. I just love it.

Santa hat, a ceramic bird, a strand of fake cranberries, a half dozen tea light votives. Whenever I retell this one to Leslie, I always add things to the list of stuff he had up his butt just for fun.[111]

5. We had a drag queen come in with a bunch of Lee Press-On Nails embedded in her cheek.

6. Councilman Bill Dexhart came in wearing a lady's one-piece bathing suit and had to get his stomach pumped because his girlfriend had forced him to drink an entire bottle of Bain de Soleil suntan oil. Ordinarily I shouldn't tell you his real name, but in this case, he bragged about it in a press conference, so I feel like it's okay.

7. One man came in who was really, really high on crystal meth. He'd painted his entire body with white house paint. He would only speak to us in clicks and beeps. We finally figured out that he thought he was R2D2.

8. This guy came in who'd tried to stand on top of a window AC unit and jump up into a tree. He didn't make it and dropped like a stone into a pile of broken car antennas. He had twenty-two puncture wounds. One of the antennas went right through his head from ear to ear, and his idiot brother kept going "You are a wild and ca-razy guy!" until the antenna guy punched him out.

9. There was a fight at the Snakehole Lounge, where this one girl threw this other girl into a dumpster and her mouth was open and she swallowed a discarded matchbox car.

10. These two cocktail waitresses at the Glitter Factory had been best friends for years, but then, one of the waitresses told the other one that her daughter needed to lose weight, or that she looked slutty or something like that. So that waitress keyed "country-ass whore" into the other's PT Cruiser. The PT Cruiser waitress then went ballistic and threw a fry daddy full of hot grease at her head.

BONUS #11 that I had forgotten about until now: This guy who was really into refurbishing old toasters and electronic stuff tried to make a homemade Theremin and electrocuted himself. When he got into the ER he made me step on his feet because he thought he had gained the power of levitation and was about to float away.

---

[111] My favorite addition ever was "eight lords a-leaping."

GREG PIKITIS

A horrible monster.

On April 13, 1994, just before dawn, a child was born at Pawnee St. Joseph's Medical Center. His mother wept. From joy? Exhaustion? Relief? It is doubtful that she herself could have even told you why, there in that most singular moment—such is the ineffable nature of childbirth. Had she, in that exhilarating instant, been able to look up from the delicate new life she held to her bosom and see me, Leslie Knope, standing by her bedside, having been transported back in time with some sort of device or by magic or something, I could have told her why she wept: she had just given birth to one of the crappiest little punks ever to walk the Earth.

Gregory Vernon Pikitis is a scourge. He may look like a towheaded little dreamboat from a Disney Channel show, but he is not. He is a punk and a criminal with a record of misdeeds longer than his enviable eyelashes. He began traipsing down his miserable immoral path at the ripe old age of eleven, when he put cement in all the holes on Pawnee Municipal Golf Course, causing one golfer to beat another golfer into a coma after throwing a temper tantrum when he shot a 19 on a par 3. After serving twenty hours of community service, Pikitis promptly filled every bottle of ketchup in JJ's Diner with non-toxic red paint. Later that year, he removed the letters "P," "E," "N," "G," "E," "R," "I," "N," and "G" from the Passenger Loading Zone sign at the Pawnee Commuter Airport.[112]

On Halloween night, 2010, however, the evil mastermind met his match. And that match was me. With the help of Andy Dwyer and courageous Officer Dave Sanderson of the Pawnee PD, I caught Pikitis in the act of spray-painting and TPing the statue of Mayor Percy in the middle of the night,[113] and I brought him to justice. Unfortunately, due to our outrageously lenient penal codes pertaining to minors, he walks our streets today, but the fact remains that I busted him so hard. Little twerp.[114]

---

[112] Full disclosure: it made me laugh really hard when I saw it, before I realized who had done it.

[113] Full disclosure: right before this happened, Andy Dwyer and I TPed Pikitis's house—a fact which I am not proud of. But it was super-fun. Also, full disclosure: Officer Dave Sanderson and I were dating at the time. I'm not sure if that's something that needs to be disclosed, but it feels like it does, so I'm fully disclosing it.

[114] Note from Greg Pikitis: Leslie is going to be so mad when she sees that I snuck this footnote in here. Suck it, Knope!

History of the Pawnee Raccoon Problem

Pawnee is famous for many things, foremost among them: raccoons. We have thousands if not hundreds of thousands of raccoons living in our town. (The word "infestation" has been used, by scientists. As has the term "raccoon blizzard.") But this wasn't always the case.

Pawnee most likely welcomed its first furry friend in 1935, possibly because from 1935 to 1946 the town was used as Eagleton's landfill. In fact, there's an old chicken-or-egg question that Pawneeans have been asking for years: "What came first? The landfill or the raccoons?" I like to think they migrated here for the trash, but it was the Pawnee hospitality that made them stay.

Pawnee raccoons can weigh as much as a five-year-old child, which, considering our obesity rate, is quite something! A popular Halloween costume used to be a raccoon, but the city council outlawed them because it became increasingly difficult to tell the people and animals apart. If you'd like to go "Rocky Spotting," their favorite time of year is summer, which has led to a colorful local aphorism: "If school's out for summer, so are those [*expletive*] raccoons."

For a brief period, Pawnee also had a possum problem. The more optimistic among us hoped they might wipe each other out, but they seemed only to make each other stronger. It's most likely just a campfire tale, but some residents swear they have seen a part-raccoon, part-possum creature that has eight legs and can run thirty miles per hour.[115] A new species! Yet another reason to come visit!

I know they give us a hard time, but I like to think it wouldn't be Pawnee without the raccoon swarm.[116]

[115] There have been no fewer than eleven public forums to attempt to decide the name of this mythological creature. To date no consensus has been reached, but the most popular suggestions are: Rassum, Poccoon, Raccposs, Possracc, Possoon, Roscum, Proscum, Porascum, Proascscuomon, and "Harbinger of Zorp."

[116] Note from Andy Dwyer: I forgot when I was making my list of previous band names that once for six hours we were called Raccoon Swarm.

Pawnee Holidays

Like any town, Pawnee has certain site-specific days that hold special meaning for us and only us. If you're here on one of these festive occasions, help us celebrate!

Toastmas (June 8)

This festive occasion falls on the anniversary of the Pawnee Bread Factory Fire in 1922. For months after that tragic event, the town still smelled like toast, which was both horrifying and delicious. Every year since, Pawneeans honor that appetizing harbinger of death by eating plain toast. As our stomachs grumble in anticipation while the hearty bread slowly turns a beautiful golden brown, we think of those who were lost. We also think, usually, "This toast would be so much better with some butter and jam."

Mayor Appreciation Day (March 29)

Established by Orlando Dombig Warm (Mayor, 1966–74), because he felt "chronically underappreciated."[117] Residents were encouraged to buy the mayor a small gift over $30. Those who did not were fined $30, which was added to the following year's Mayor Appreciation Day fund.

Beverly Kiln Day (May 22)

Pawnee has its own version of Sadie Hawkins Day, unwittingly created by former Pawnee city councilman Rudge Hullerby. At the ripe old age of seventy-eight, Hullerby found himself madly in love with seventeen-year-old Beverly Kiln, the daughter of one of his fellow city councilmen, Doug Kiln. After his confession of love for Kiln's daughter was met with a disapproving punch in the face, Hullerby hastily added an amendment to the city constitution, forming a holiday wherein single men over seventy could ask out teenage girls.

Hullerby's advances—holiday or no—were rebuffed by Ms. Kiln. And to this day, "Beverly Kiln Day" is celebrated in Pawnee with a daylong teaching session wherein high school girls are warned about creepy old men who make advances on them.

---

[117] Mayor Warm served for eight years, and in that time, accomplished basically zero in the way of "things." Among the "successes" he took credit for were (a) the town not being overrun by weevils, as it had been twenty years earlier, and (b) the sales of the Rolling Stones' *Beggars Banquet*. He was not in any way "underappreciated."

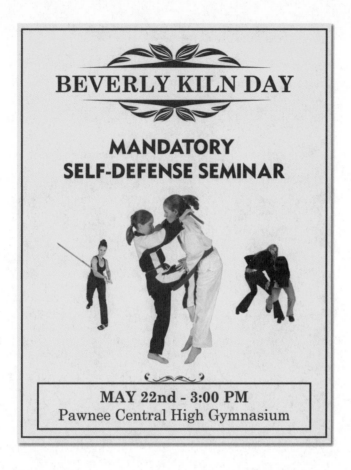

Eagleton Day (July 14)

Every July 14, Eagleton citizens gather to celebrate the day their ancestors left Pawnee for good. And every year, on the same day, Pawnee teens celebrate Eagleton Day by sneaking over the town line to play a prank on Eagleton, in order to pay them back for being such snobby jerky buttfaces.

Past pranks include: freezing the town water supply, replacing all the zoo animals with stuffed animals, contaminating the water supply, siphoning the water supply to Pawnee, and completely draining the water supply. Most Eagletonians now spend Eagleton Day guarding their reservoir, which is doubly awesome, because now they can't even enjoy their own holiday. God, they're just the worst.

The day after Eagleton Day is an unofficial holiday called "Reunion Day," in which people from Pawnee head over to bail their family members out of Eagleton jails.

111

A TRIP DOWN
MEMORY LANE:
PAWNEE

The Leaping Stag Saloon, 1948. Pawnee's drinking age was changed from nine to eighteen in 1973.

ABOVE: Sweetums assembly line, nightshift, 1899.

BELOW: Zion Canyon, one of America's most stunning national parks, is not located in Pawnee. But still—it's gorgeous!

OPPOSITE: **"Fire Gentleman"** Josiah Gremph attempts to repel the Great Pawnee Fire of 1896 with a skillet. That year, Gremph created the nation's first "Gentlemen's Fire Fighting Corps" in order to "tame damnable infernos with displays of manly virtue." The Corps rejected the use of water or hoses, with the idea that they were not sporting, or gentlemanly, thus limiting themselves to "whatsoever object the fire-fighter finds at hand." The Corps, like its founder, was short-lived.

ABOVE: The Ramsett Park Civil War Memorial honors the seventeen brave Pawneeans who died to preserve the Union. The obelisk to its right honors the nineteen Pawneeans who died while constructing the Civil War Memorial.

OPPOSITE: In 1943, women at the Sweetums factory pack bottles of "Patriot Fuel," a concoction of melted red licorice, white confectioners' sugar, and blue dye. Though Sweetums' nefarious owners were secretly supporting the German war effort, it was also the exclusive food supplier to the Seventeenth Armored Tank Division. By the end of World War II, the "Wolf Pack" boasted the highest number of destroyed German Panzer tanks and the highest rate of type-2 diabetes in the army.

In 1853, dignitaries arrive at the stately home of Mayor Christian Christianssen,
Pawnee's wealthiest citizen.

The 1917 Founders Day celebration, featuring the annual "Tournament of Whores" parade.
This Shame Float is carrying the women in town who over the past year had exposed their
calves in public.

From the cover of the *Pawnee Journal*'s 1938 Valentine's Day supplement: two young lovers take a romantic stroll during the period known as "The Bad Smell" (1937–1940).

LEFT: In 1905, a group of industrialists started work on the Chicago/New York Electric Rail Road, which would connect those two metropolises with trains that could top one hundred miles per hour.[118] Pawneeans were delighted to learn that our city was to be the main Indiana hub for the rail system, but the economy collapsed and the line was never finished. They did leave us with a one-and-a-half-block railroad system on Laughing Squaw Lane, running from Shove It! Storage Solutions all the way to the empty building where the Dollar General used to be. Trips last four minutes and cost $11.00; seniors ride free after 10 P.M.

RIGHT: The landmark service station on Stachester Street in Pawnee was once owned by the colorful Francis "Fanny" Duggars. Fanny was known for his speedy, friendly full service and would delight customers with whimsical folk songs he composed himself, about Pawnee life. Drivers from all over Indiana were regaled with ditties such as "Ruby's Pale Lantern," "Pop Pop Popping Corn," and "That Little Ol' Rooster Down on Poppy's Farm." Fanny passed away in 1952 by his own hand (auto-erotic asphyxiation).

[118] This led to the painting of Spirit of Pawnee, one of the most awful objects in the universe (see "City Hall Murals," page 165).

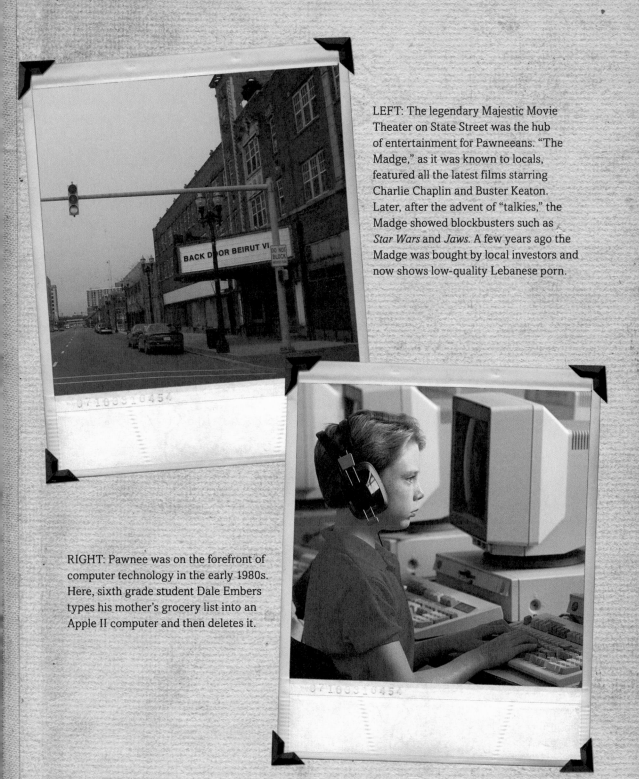

LEFT: The legendary Majestic Movie Theater on State Street was the hub of entertainment for Pawneeans. "The Madge," as it was known to locals, featured all the latest films starring Charlie Chaplin and Buster Keaton. Later, after the advent of "talkies," the Madge showed blockbusters such as *Star Wars* and *Jaws.* A few years ago the Madge was bought by local investors and now shows low-quality Lebanese porn.

RIGHT: Pawnee was on the forefront of computer technology in the early 1980s. Here, sixth grade student Dale Embers types his mother's grocery list into an Apple II computer and then deletes it.

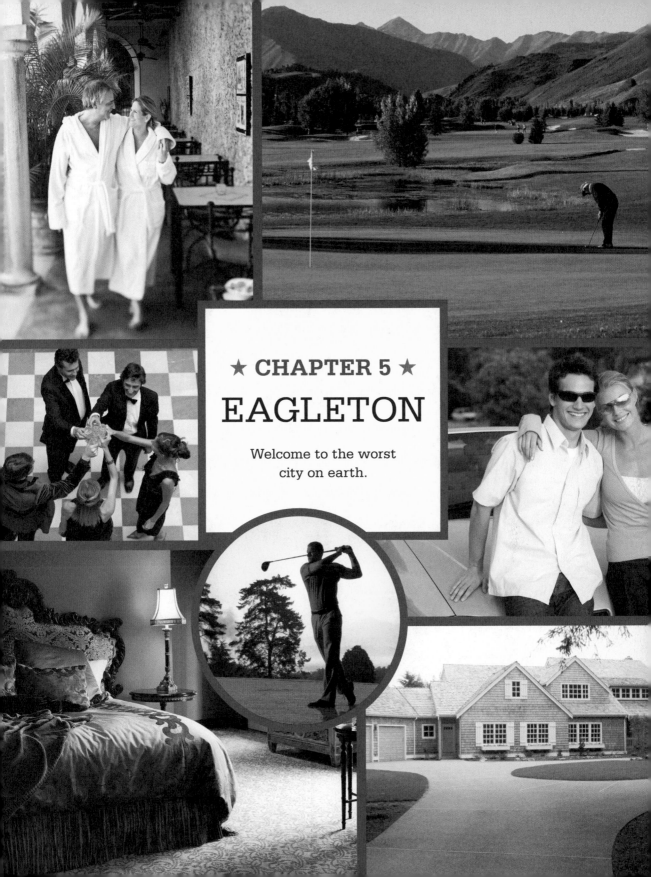

★ CHAPTER 5 ★
EAGLETON

Welcome to the worst
city on earth.

5

Introduction

Just to the west of our fair city lies a small, vanilla-scented jerk farm called Eagleton, which, although beautiful, is populated by 9,500 of the biggest ass-faces you have ever met.

Shortly after Pawnee was founded in May of 1817, a group of the wealthiest and most prominent citizens, finding the soil untenable and the smell unpleasant, "evacuated" to the west and founded Eagleton. That dickish spirit still permeates the town today, as they sit up on their hill (yes, the entire town is slightly elevated) and look down their noses at everything Pawnee. You know that feeling you get when you go to a restaurant in jeans and a T-shirt and you didn't realize it was a slightly fancy restaurant, and you feel like everyone is looking at you and judging you? That's the way we feel all the time when we go to Eagleton. Even if we're in formal wear. God I hate them.

Feel free to visit if you like boring people boring your ears off with boring conversations about how amazing their lives are. But I'm warning you: they suck.

Eagleton at a Glance

Incorporated: 1817

Population (a/o 2010 census): 9,480 arrogant pinheads

Mayor: His Royal Highness, the Right Honorable Baron Fartface von Lickmybutt

Median Household Income: More money than any of them could spend in a lifetime

Highest Point: There are no high points in Eagleton. Only low points.

Lowest Point: The "bottoming-out" feeling you get when you are there

Denonym: (a) Eagletonian, (b) Turdbrain

Sister Cities: Any city that has ever housed, aided, abetted, or given succor to international criminals

Official City Tree: The trees in *Wizard of Oz* that attack people with apples and try to kill them

Official City Bird: The flying monkeys from *Wizard of Oz* that attack people and try to kill them

Official City Drink: A steaming hot cup of their own pee

Largest Employers: These landed gentry, born-on-third-thought-they-hit-a-triple trust-fund babies wouldn't know an honest day's work if it bit them on their overstuffed wallets.[119]

Demographics: For all its faults, Eagleton is a wonderfully diverse town, as evidenced by the pie chart below.

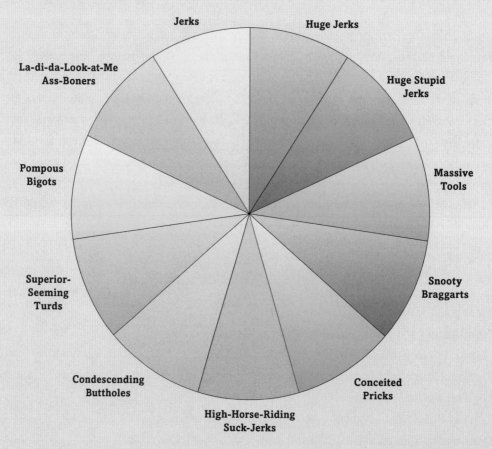

---

[119] A lot of them are doctors at Pawnee St. Joe's. And some run hedge funds. Whatever. They stink.

Traitors!

A recent poll[120] reveals that 100 percent of all Pawneeans think that Eagleton rots. However, three years ago, longtime Pawnee restauranteurs Tim and Millie Mims opened their popular eatery **Jurassic Fork** (2190 Valerian Road) over the border in Eagleton, to take advantage of its favorable business climate and clean running water. Unfortunately, many of our own citizens (I'm looking at you, Jerry Gergich) have begun taking the trip to the dark side to continue to enjoy Jurassic Fork's "Bron-toast-saurus." Idiots.

Jurassic Fork represents the Mims' most successful restaurant endeavor to date—it has already been open far longer than their many other, now-closed, Steven Spielberg–themed restaurants: Raiders of the Lost Fork, Close Encounters of the Third Tine, E.Tea, Munch (a play on *Munich*), Catch Meat If You Can, Schindler's Lunch, Empire of the Bun, and Amistad.

Schindler's Lunch was hailed by one local restaurant critic as: "The most depressing place I have ever been."

[120] Poll conducted by Leslie Knope. Poll question: "Which of these statements best describes you as a person? A: "I think Eagleton is great, and I am a perverted weirdo who has sex dreams about camels." B: "I hate Eagleton, and I am well liked and have many friends." MOE +/- 17%.

EAGLETON VS. PAWNEE

Eagleton/Pawnee Football Rivalry
by Andy Dwyer

What's up, guys and gals? Andy Dwyer here, former Pawnee Central football star and current lead singer/guitarist for the band Mouse Rat. Check out our website at www.mouseratmusic.com. Or net? Or gov or something. I forget. I'll ask Burly when he gets home from work.

I'm here to tell you about the most famous high school football rivalry in all of the world of Indiana. My old school, the Pawnee Central Puppies vs. the Eagleton Jaguars. What a dumb mascot. Who's scared of jaguars? Maybe baby dogs, but that's it.

Anyways, this game has been played on Thanksgiving day every season for the past seventy-eight years. Except for one year, because of the raccoon uprising. And then it wasn't played the next year due to the revenge of the raccoons, after we thwarted their uprising. Here are a few of the most famous games: *(You should listen to music while you read this. When I read I like to listen to music sometimes. And hey—Mouse Rat is music! That's what you should listen to. Buy our CD at www.mouseratmusic. . . Man, I wanna say .gov, but that seems wrong. Just try them all. You'll find it.)*

1932 EAGLETON 75, PAWNEE 0

The first game ever played between these two teams. Pawnee didn't yet have helmets or shoes, and the team only had five guys on it. I'm not even sure they knew what football was yet. That would all change the next year though . . .

Pawnee Central High Fight Song

Music and Lyrics by Lawrence F. Norwing (class of 2003)

We are the Lightning of Pawnee!
Fight on, fight on, fight on!
Formerly known as the Red Scalpers
The name was changed due to Native American protests

We were briefly called the Red Men for a time
Again, changed after protests
Then very briefly called the Crazyfarts McCools
After a poll was conducted among the student body

Then we were the Pawnee Central Puppies
The thinking being that no one can complain about a puppy
Then someone did for some reason, now lost to history,
And now we are the Pawnee Lightning!

So, fight on, fight on, the orange and orange!
Formerly the orange and black
But black was removed from the school colors due
    to gang activity
Gang members were wearing Pawnee Central colors
    to represent their gang membership

So now we wear orange trimmed with orange
And we will triumph o'er the Jaguars of Eagleton
As we have once before in 1992
Fight on, fight on, Pawnee Central High!
Formerly known as Pawnee Remedial School
    for Habitual Offenders

1933 EAGLETON 88, PAWNEE 6

That's right! Pawnee scored a touchdown! The Pawnee running back, Charles Bundle, thought he was scoring on his own end zone (he was paid to throw the game), but he got confused and ended up accidentally scoring an actual touchdown. Bundle was almost sent to prison for accepting a bribe, but because he was so dumb and scored in the wrong end zone, he didn't have to go to prison. Then later he was sent to prison for murder.

1954 EAGLETON 41, PAWNEE 27

Because Eagleton had won like a thousand times in a row, they spotted Pawnee 28 points, which explains why this was such a nail-biter. Then Pawnee played so bad the refs actually took a point away.

1992 PAWNEE 20, EAGLETON 12

We won this one! Eat it, Eagleton. This ended their streak of like a billion wins in a row. Basically, this win was the result of two main things: Pawnee had an awesome QB named Tom Dissellio who went on to play D1 football at Butler, and this was his senior year game and he was awesome. I was a kid but I was there and he was amazing. Also, the other thing that helped is that Eagleton's like forty best players were caught smoking weed the night before and were suspended, so they only had like twelve guys and filled the rest of their roster with long distance runners and dudes from their Renaissance Madrigals Choir. One dude dressed like a court jester had like 110 yards rushing.

1998 EAGLETON 48, PAWNEE 17

My last game with the team, and probably my best memory of being on the team. So here's what happened: I was a linebacker mostly, but the game was super physical. There was a big fight, and our first- and second-string QB's both broke all of their legs. So Pawnee brought in the big guns. Then, the referee ejected all the players who brought out big guns (no shots were fired). Then, they put me in at QB! I did kind of awesome—threw two TD passes and led us to the highest point total of the year. It was my "Rudy" moment, except we got killed.

That's it, guys! Hope you had as much fun reading this as I did reading it!

—ANDY RADICAL

Eagleton: Don't Go There

O ne of Pawnee's favorite pastimes is crapping on Eagleton. For a while there, Pawnee's favorite pastime was *literally* crapping on Eagleton, but there was a huge police crackdown, so now we just like to make fun of them.

In the spirit of crapping on Eagleton, here are some of the top must-miss sights that you should definitely not go to:

Eagleton Plaza A small strip of hoity-toity stores where ladies with facelifts go to buy serums.

Eagleton Gap It's like every other Gap, but the awning is in earth tones. Big whoop. Besides, who needs a Gap when you can stay in Pawnee and shop at Dorothy's Discount Dresses—"The second 'D' is for Discount!"

Arcadia Spa Everything costs like $500 minimum. How relaxing does that sound? Maybe you should just give them your bank account number and routing information. It might be more convenient for them to access all your money that way.

Knotted Oak Ampitheatre and Concert Venue Eagleton wastes taxpayer money on a fiscally irresponsible state-of-the-art concert venue that attracts pop stars (if you can even call Paul Simon a "star" anymore) and international touring acts. Way to give local talent a chance, Eagleton.

Eagleton Pool at Lily Canyon This is a public pool, but everyone judges your suit and body, and outsiders are not welcome.[121]

Saddle Ridge Country Club & Golf Course Sorry, I just fell asleep. What were we talking about?

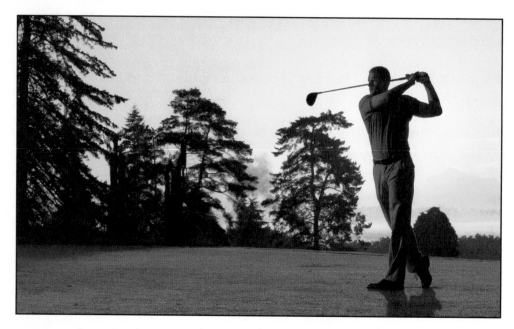

Saddle Ridge Country Club Horse Stables Go here if you want to meet weird rich women who can't connect with human beings.

Eagleton Chinatown Doesn't exist, so you're missing it whether you want to or not.

Eagleton International Film Festival This thing is such a joke. William Hurt showed up *once* and now they think their poop don't stink.

Eagleton Reservoir If I wanted to see super-skinny ladies in designer sweat suits walking in circles while they complain about their nannies, I'd go there, because that's all you see there.

---

[121] Note from Tom Haverford: I do kind of have to give it up to the ladies of Eagleton, who, as a general rule, are keepin' it tyyyyyght.

Anti-Eagleton Slurs

Regalton Pawneeans say "Regalton" with a snooty British accent to imply that Eagletonians think they are royalty and rule the planet, which they are not and do not. Some Eagletonians have actually adopted that phony British accent that Madonna uses, which makes this probably our most accurate slur.

Eagle-town A simple one where we pretend we think it's pronounced "Eagle-town" and don't know it's "Eagle-*tunn*." They hate this. They get all huffy and haughty, and then you hit them with "Regalton."

A-hole-ton Pretty self-explanatory. Originated at a tailgate party. It was just a super-drunk Pawnee kid slurring his words, but this is what it sounded like, so it stuck.

Bald Eagle-ton Insult for bald guys in Eagleton. Doesn't get much use, because they all buy plugs.

Beagleton Not our best, but the idea was that they seem like the type of people to have beagles as pets, instead of a more down-to-earth dog, like a collie or something. What do you want? I said it wasn't our best.

Cannibals Did you know an eagle usually hatches two eaglets but the biggest one sometimes eats the smallest one? Pawnee ornithologists do, so they taunt Eagletonian ornithologists with this.

Sparrowton Said because sparrows are small, common birds with stubby beaks—far less impressive birds than eagles. Also a favorite with the Pawnee bird-watching set.

"EAGER-TON!" Headline in the *Pawnee Journal* after Eagleton lost a track and field event, because Eagleton's entrant had jumped the gun and was disqualified from the race.

Loserton It's not smart, but it gets the job done in a pinch.

Evilton See above.

Greedyton See the two above.

Anti-Pawnee Slurs

Here is what those condescending buttholes say about us:

Scrawnee Eagleton's Little League dads chant this at our boys. Just poor sportsmanship. Uncalled for.

Spawnee of Satan Who came up with that? An idiot?

Blah-nee In 1998, the *Eagleton Tribune* panned the proposed Pawnee Downtown Revitalization Plan using this term, and unfortunately it stuck. But the joke is on them, because like one year later the Pawnee Downtown Revitalization Plan was completely abandoned.

Yawnee Slur that implies we are boring. Or maybe Eagletonians are just tired because they can't sleep at night because they are terrible people haunted by visions of their horrible deeds.

Pee Knee This clearly makes no sense and doesn't even sound like "Pawnee." Yet another example of stupidity on Eagleton's part. Stupid, stupid, stupid.

Idiots A lot of times they just call us idiots. Real creative, dum-dums.

Gerrymandering!: Cool Things Pawnee Has Lost to Eagleton Over the Years

From the very beginning, Eagleton has drawn and redrawn our common town line, in order to absorb or steal everything cool in Pawnee. Here's a list of things they've gerrymandered over the years:

Hartley Hill This was the highest point in Pawnee until Eagleton seceded and built its entire town on it. Their mistake. Do you know how vulnerable you are on a hill? People can fire guns up at you.

---

[122] A stunningly beautiful mural of this wildflower meadow hangs on the second floor of Pawnee City Hall, and it's my favorite place in the building. I can tell a lot about whether I am compatible with a person based on whether the person likes this mural. Also, its presence in City Hall means I can look at those wildflowers anytime I want, so, point Pawnee!

Longview Wildflower Meadow A stunning, naturally occurring wildflower meadow that once served as the northwest corner of our town was "claimed" by Eagleton in 1922. So what. Why would I want to walk through a field of mud and bees to look at a wildflower when I can just go online and look at every flower in the world?[122]

6 Sizeable Ponds Whatever. We have three swimming pools.

35,000 Acres of Fertile Farming Land That one stung.

Natural Curative Hot Springs Don't need this. We have doctors, thanks. (A lot of our doctors actually did leave to go to Eagleton. Better benefits. And curative hot springs.)

K. Peterson Lewis Art Museum K. Peterson Lewis Fart Museum.

Goldmine Also stung. But it's empty now, so eff them.

★ CHAPTER 6 ★

HEROES & ALL-STARS

I was once asked, in a college admissions interview, who were the five people from history I would like to have dinner with. My answer was: "Pawnee has been home to so many amazing and fascinating personalities, selecting only five would be too difficult." Then the guy said, "They don't all have to be from your hometown," and I said, "I know, but they would be." And he said, "So you would choose some random city councilman over, say, Abe Lincoln?" and I said "Maybe so—I love my hometown, and I'd relish the chance to meet those who came before me and helped shape it into the place it is today," and he said, "That's weird," and I yelled, "Amherst is weird!" Which wasn't smart, but I probably wasn't getting in anyway.[123]

The point is that, like every town, Pawnee has borne a handful of exceptional people who deserve to be remembered forever, via books just like this one. Come meet them, won't you?

[123] I was wait-listed, and actually got in off the wait-list, but decided to go to IU instead, and I had an awesome time and got a great education for like zero dollars, so take that, snobby Amherst guy.

6

DOROTHY EVERTON SMYTHE

COURAGE, HONOR, PANTS: THE STORY OF A TRUE HEROINE
by Leslie Knope

(Pawnee resident, amateur historian, feminist, and 2010 winner
of the Dorothy Everton Smythe Female Empowerment Award[124])

Ladies: what are you wearing right now? Something comfortable? Pants, perhaps? Well, I want you to imagine a world where just for wearing those pants, you would be thrown in prison. Then I want you to thank Dorothy Everton Smythe.

Born in 1891, to Margaret Ann Madison and Rutherford Smythe, Dorothy grew up the only girl among eight children. Some might say that that's where she got her rough-and-tumble spirit. But they'd be wrong, as four of her brothers turned out to be gay, and

LEFT: Dorothy Everton Smythe, age eleven, bundling hay as part of her daily chores at the insane asylum to which she was sent after declaring she wanted to grow up to be President.

---

[124] Technically, the award was issued to Parks Department Director Ron Swanson, in an attempt by the Indiana Organization of Women to prove a point; namely, that giving a man a "Female Empowerment Award" would attract more media attention than giving it to a woman. To me, it proved the point that feminist groups can be just as cynical and stupid as other kinds of groups, which is a good lesson. Anyway, Ron—who actually is a feminist, in his own way, in that he is blind to all evaluative measures other than self-possessedness and fondness for red meat—fully admitted both publicly and privately that I had done all the work that led to the award being given to him, and later (and correctly) turned the award over to me in a spontaneous public ceremony/train wreck at the Indiana Organization of Women Annual Awards Dinner. So even though it has his name on it, it is my award, is what I'm saying, and I'm proud to have won it. Also, n.b. for all of you out there who might have someone win an award which you really deserved to win, only to have the person then movingly present it to you and restore your faith in humanity, justice, and friendship all at the same time: you cannot just cross the person's name out with a Sharpie and write yours in above it. It doesn't look cool and punk rock, as it was intended to—it just looks sloppy. Spring for the new nameplate.

the other three were generally kind of wimpy. The youngest, Devon, died at the age of twenty, when he was struck by a horse carriage while fleeing a chipmunk.[125]

When Dorothy was four years old, she marched into her father's study and declared aloud, "I shall be President one day." She was immediately sent to live in a sanitarium for twelve years.[126] It was this hardscrabble childhood experience that made her into the woman she became.

Upon exiting, and taking stock of the oppressive culture of Pawnee in the early twentieth century, Dorothy realized she would not be getting much help in achieving her dreams. Not only were women not allowed to vote, a series of antiquated laws and local customs prohibited women from reading in public, challenging facts proffered by men, mentioning the President's name, discussing the news, or "getting lippy."[127] She thus set about to secretly educate herself, mostly from texts she stole from men she "entertained." "I traded kisses for books," she wrote in her diary, "a deal from which I certainly came out ahead!" Basically, she was a little slutty, but for a good cause.

Dorothy was an eloquent speaker. She became known for standing on an apple box in the town square and delivering speeches. Her first speech was an impassioned plea for people to stop trying to look up her skirt when she was on the apple box. Her most famous speech, "What Salary, for a Child?" was about the treatment of children (mostly boys aged six to ten) who worked at the Sweetums factory. Dorothy was deeply opposed to this, as the nine-year-old boys were paid substantially more than adult female employees.

THE PANTS PERIOD

One cold winter morning, at the age of twenty-four, Dorothy Everton Smythe decided to wear pants. The temperature that day was seventeen degrees, a record low, so her decision seems reasonable. The only problem? It was a Sunday. Pants-wearing by women on a Sunday was illegal and forbidden.[128] But Smythe, fed up with the oppressive,

---

[125] An onlooker described the scene thus: "To call his screams 'girlish' is insulting to girls. No girl has ever screamed that high, for that long, for any reason."

[126] The Pawnee Institute for Hysterical Women and Rowdy House Pets.

[127] Women could also not "walk unduly quickly," "wave their elbows about," say the words "naughty" or "calipers," or draw likenesses of the human anatomy unless both they and the likenesses were wearing full-length overcoats. It was also believed by Pawnee medical practitioners that too much "imagination" led to sterilization.

[128] As was wearing gloves before noon. And "not being pregnant." It was a strange time.

misogynistic rules, put on those pants, strode confidently out her door, and was immediately arrested by like forty cops. The first one on the scene blew a riot whistle, and literally forty cops and a dozen firefighters showed up and basically panicked—one of them turned a fire hose on Smythe, and another blew an air raid siren that rallied an army unit stationed nearby, who marched into the town en masse and briefly declared martial law. Clearly, she had ruffled some feathers.

When asked why she wore pants, Dorothy simply and elegantly replied, "I was cold." Later, perhaps trying to make the moment more memorable, she amended her comment by adding, "I was cold—cold of being a second-class citizen!" When it was pointed out that this was confusing and meaningless, she amended her comment again and said,

"By treating women as second-class citizens, our town was frozen in time. But I was also literally freezing. So . . . I was cold." Years later, she added, "I fought for my freedom one leg at a time. Is that something?"

Her actions inspired other Pawnee women to wear pants,[129] and soon many more budding feminists joined the fight. The male-dominated city council saw their jails filling up with women protesting these arcane laws, and knew what they had to do: they swiftly voted to build the first Pawnee Women's Prison. (Yet another advancement for which we can thank Dorothy Everton Smythe.)

Dorothy spent four years in jail. While there, she wrote her now-famous tract *It Was Cold, I Was*

LEFT: Actress Paige Wimbley in a 1948 production of Dabney Clough-Shivers's One Leg at a Time: The Dorothy Everton Smythe Story. *Ironically, Wimbley was arrested after wearing pants during previews.*

---

[129] Oddly, Smythe was vehemently opposed to shorts. She thought they made her calves look weird.

Cold, Everything Was Cold, So I Wore Pants: One Woman's Decision to Wear Pants Because It Was Cold.[130] Ironically, it was illegal for women to read it in public until 1938. Burning it, however, was perfectly legal, if not encouraged; thus, even more ironically, when it got cold in winter, women who were still prohibited from wearing pants would often burn it to keep warm.

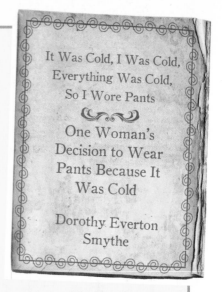

It Was Cold, I Was Cold, Everything Was Cold, So I Wore Pants

One Woman's Decision to Wear Pants Because It Was Cold

Dorothy Everton Smythe

POST-PANTS PERIOD

Her incarceration eventually led to a public outcry for change, and in concert with the larger Women's Suffrage Movement sweeping the nation, many of the statutes prohibiting women's equality were overturned. At the age of forty, Smythe was "sworn in" as the first female judge in the Pawnee Municipal Court system. It was purely an honorary position, but never one to back down from a challenge, she found a technicality in the municipal code and insisted on overseeing more than one thousand cases. She has the city record for mistrials.

Smythe passed away in October of 1947, and in 1948 the Indiana Organization of Women founded the Dorothy Everton Smythe Female Empowerment Award, which would be used every year to recognize strong, powerful, intelligent women who are generally amazing and great.[131]

LEFT: 1942. A be-pantsed Dorothy smiles knowing she has won an incredible victory for all women and because her pants are keeping her legs from getting chilly.

---

[130] I find it to be riveting, but it was mostly panned by critics. "Given the bravery of her decision, the text itself is disappointingly and startlingly dull. Also, riddled with spelling errors and confusing turns of phrase," wrote one jerk.

[131] Full disclosure: I won the award in 2010. (See footnote 124, *supra*.)

Other Pawnee Feminist Pioneers

1. Sally Musslore pretended to be a man to sneak into male-only areas of town. She was the first person in Indiana history to hold her index finger under her nose as a fake-mustache disguise.

2. Polly Green-Hastings once cut off all her hair to prove a point after a male store clerk refused to sell her tobacco. She got her tobacco and cured her lice simultaneously, so: win-win.

3. Agnes Porter first female graduate of Pawnee Technical College, the first female anesthesiologist in the *whole state of Indiana*, and the first woman in Pawnee to say "Watch yourself, buster," to an unwanted butt-pincher. Her life is chronicled in her autobiography, *Gas-hole: Confessions of a Lady Anesthesiologist.*

4. Jane Sterpingle On November 4, 1919, Sterpingle went to City Hall and attempted to vote in the local elections. She raised such a fuss when reminded that she could not, she was thrown in jail. Sterpingle was also the first woman in Pawnee to write a check, which was for her own bail, to get herself out of jail for trying to vote in the local election. Unfortunately, it was against the law in Pawnee to write a check if you were a woman, so immediately upon posting bail she was put back in jail. Upon appearing in front of the judge to argue the absurdity of this case, Sterpingle used the term "Möbius strip," and the judge thought she was swearing at him, which was illegal for a woman, so she was thrown back in jail.

5. Elsa Clack One of the first women to circumnavigate the globe-shaped building at Epcot Center.

Pawnee's Greatest Athletes

"Gentleman" Jim Shorter Shorter was one of the greatest bare-knuckle boxers in Indiana history. His punching power was legendary, and he killed multiple men, many in the boxing ring. "Shorter Kills Irishman" was a frequent headline in the 1890s. Shorter never backed down from a challenge. His career came to a premature end when, after being goaded by a fight promoter, he agreed to box a horse. The horse knocked Shorter out in the fifty-eighth round and went on to become the Indiana State Champion for three years.

Edward Wu, Baseball Edward Wu was born in Pawnee in 1976. In 1978 he and his family moved to Trumbull, Connecticut, where he would go on to be a backup utility infielder on the team that won the Little League World Series in 1989. Wu is currently a tax professional at the H&R Block in Irvine, California, and was inducted into the Pawnee Sports Hall of Fame in 2009.[132]

---

[132] Didn't even show up to his own induction ceremony. You're dead to me, Wu.

Beverly Shawver, Shot Put Born in South Pawnee, Beverly Shawver put the world on notice when she won a bronze medal in the women's shot put at the 1986 Goodwill Games. Although she never medaled in an international event again, Shawver continued to consistently place in the top fifty until her retirement in 1992. In 1994 it was revealed that Beverly Shawver was born a man, Matthew Shawver.

Tatiana Gurylenko, Rhythmic Gymnastics The elegant, Russian-born Gurylenko "sprang" onto the rhythmic gymnastic scene with an electrifying performance at the 1983 Pan-American Games, though she was ultimately disqualified when her routine exceeded the allotted ninety-second time limit by over fourteen minutes. Gurylenko recovered at the 1987 games—held in nearby Indianapolis!—and placed fourth, much to the pride of her adopted home state. Gurylenko retired

in 1988 and became the physical education teacher at Pawnee Central High School. In 1998 it was revealed that Tatiana Gurylenko was born a man, Craig Snorpley.

Jessica "Mark" Eveland, Golf Jessica "Mark" Eveland is widely acknowledged to be the greatest female golfer to ever hit the links in Pawnee. Eveland was known for her slashing lefty swing, her incredible touch around the greens, and her inexplicable demand to be nicknamed "Mark." "Call me Mark," Eveland insisted. "Why? No reason. It's my nickname, that's all. My real name is Jessica, but my nickname is 'Mark.'" Career highlights include almost playing in the 1974 LPGA Championship and meeting LPGA golfer Se Ri Pak. In 1996 it was revealed that Jessica "Mark" Eveland was indeed biologically a woman, to the surprise of many.

Other Athletes of Note

Joey Posnanski Attempted half-court shot during a 2006 game between the Pacers and the Washington Wizards. Overly bouncy, probably-sabotaged rim prevented him from winning a Toyota Tacoma. Did win $100 Gift Card to Papa Johns.

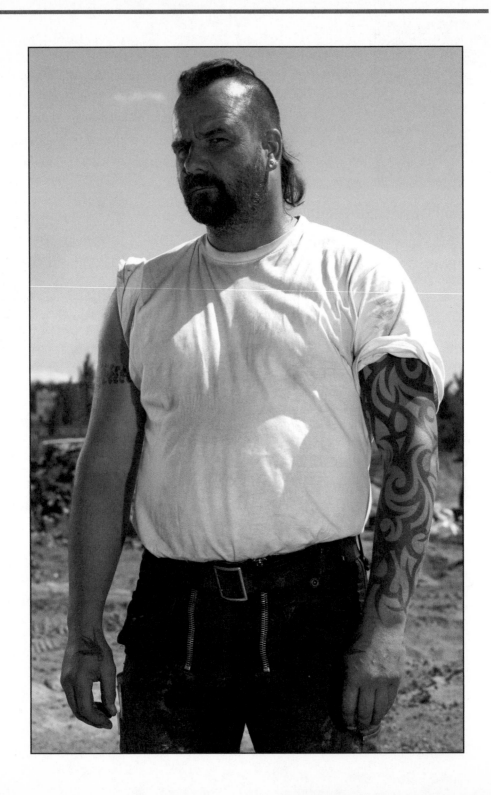

Howard Fint *(right)* Indiana State mini-golf champion, once featured in *ESPN: The Magazine*, in an article entitled "It's Not a Waste of Time to Him."

Mike Shoemaker Has forty-nine of the top fifty high scores on Golden Tee Live 2008 at Scully's Bar.[133]

Tom Dissellio Star quarterback of the 1992 Pawnee Central High football team.[134] Later played in college and is definitely somewhere amazing doing something amazing.

Jeff Blundt *(left)* "The Laser Ninja"—"pro" wrestler. Two-time Exxtream (sic) Midwest Wrestling League Champ. Known for his signature "Double Lazer" finishing move and his 2007 arrest for selling crystal meth in the parking lot of a clown college.

Margie and Russell Gummersall Members of the 2007 U.S. National Korfball team that, as you know, placed thirteenth in the World Championship in Abborrtjarn, Sweden. Korfball is a coed game played in many northern European countries. It's like basketball without a backboard. It was introduced to the Pawnee school system in 1920 by longtime Pawnee middle school gym teacher, Magnus Olafson, who played the game as a boy back in Sweden. It has been very popular with Pawneeans for decades, perhaps explaining why Pawnee, unlike virtually all of its surrounding towns, has never been great at basketball.

Emma-Jean Holsapple Catcher for the Sweetums Sugar Queens, a barnstorming women's baseball team that played several exhibition games in the mid-1920s. As often happens with important events in herstory, almost no record remains of the Sugar Queens. But I am 99 percent sure that Emma-Jean Holsapple looked exactly like Geena Davis and melted the heart of her cranky, drunk manager who looked exactly like Tom Hanks (circa *Bachelor Party*; not bloated Hanks).

---

[133] As of the time of publication. Also as of the time of publication, number 41 is "ASS."

[134] I have been unable to find his statistics anywhere but rest assured, he was awesome. And, having sat behind him in homeroom, I can also assure you his hair smelled amazing.

Paint Along with Pauline

Until 1986, Pawnee was home to WWIQ, our very own public television station. Channel 36 played all the PBS favorites that kids loved—*Sesame Street, Mister Rogers' Neighborhood*, interminable pledge drives, and *The Electric Company*. But every Wednesday at 4:00 P.M., we all tuned in for some local flavor.

Pauline Schwinn-Blem had taught art at Wamapoke Elementary for eleven years, and when her youngest kid went off to college, the empty-nester told her friend (and WWIQ program director) Maureen Cranwitch that she was looking for something to do, and *Paint Along with Pauline* was born. The thirteen episodes of *Paint Along with Pauline* originally aired during WWIQ's inaugural season, in 1969, but were rerun every week until the station went off the air seventeen years later.[135]

Each episode, the telegenic forty-two-year-old would appear on a spare set next to a blank canvas and invite viewers to join her on a "journey of creation." Then she would walk them, step-by-step, through the production of a sweet little landscape painting. It was a great show, if a little snoozy—particularly the second half hour of the show, when you literally watched paint dry. But it was weirdly addictive. To this day, Pawneeans of a certain age can bond by rattling off the names of the paint colors Pauline used in each episode—"Pthalo Blue, Alizarin Crimson, Cadmium Yellow," and so on. Some of us still have paintings we made as we followed her instructions to "make a happy little seagull" or "give that lonely tree a buddy." At least one of us still has several dozen of these paintings stacked in her upstairs linen closet.[136]

If the show was so beloved that people happily watched the same reruns over and over for more than a decade, why did they stop production after one season, you ask? I sat down with Kurt Zurn, critic at large for the *Pawnee Journal*. He has been researching *Paint Along with Pauline* for a profile of Ms. Schwinn-Blem that he someday hopes to get printed in some sort of fancy magazine that people read in New York and stuff. He had obtained copies of all thirteen episodes that aired . . . plus, to my delight, he had unearthed a fourteenth, "Lost Episode" that had never aired at all! Here is a transcript of our conversation:

[*We are in Zurn's small craftsman house on Houdsdale Street, watching episode 3.*]

Leslie Knope: This is great! I haven't seen this in years. I remember this episode!

---

[135] The 1985 Fall Pledge Drive yielded zero donations, despite its well-publicized slogan, "This Time We Really Mean It." I miss WWIQ, but jeez, guys, you can only cry wolf so many times.

[136] And no, I will not throw them out. I don't care what the guy on *Hoarders* says.

Kurt Zurn: You do?

LK: Of course! She's going to put a stream right there! [*In the lilting tones of Pauline.*] "And now let's dab in a fun little bridge. The stream has a friend!"

KZ: Wow. You weren't kidding.

LK: Sorry. Just a little excited. She was amazing.

KZ: Right. So, this is classic *Paint Along with Pauline*, okay? You've got your nature scene. It's idealized but, y'know, true to life. A stream. Some mountains. A stand of trees . . .

LK: [*spot-on impression of Pauline*] "A little gaggle of evergreens!"

KZ: Sure. It's basically like this through episode 10.

LK: [*excitedly*] The one with the birch trees surrounding the little frozen pond with the deer tracks in the snow!

KZ: Wow. Yes. But then: episode 11.

LK: The polka-dot sky!

KZ: The polka-dot sky.

[*Zurn skips ahead to episode 11. It is just as I remember it. It is as though I painted along with this episode a hundred times. Pauline is just going along like normal, filling in the foliage with her number 6 Fan Brush, and then she kind of shudders for a second, pauses for a very long time, and then starts putting these big red polka-dots in the sky and doesn't say anything else for the whole rest of the episode. It is mesmerizing.*]

LK: She makes two hundred and seventy-seven dots! When I was a kid, I counted them.

KZ: I believe you. Have you ever wondered why she made those dots?

LK: Well, because . . . because the sky . . . No, actually, I haven't.

KZ: In my research, I discovered that when Pauline's kids went off to school, she, shall we say, took advantage of their absence.

[*Zurn opens up a folder of photographs of Pauline Schwinn-Blem from the fall of 1969. Here's Pauline dropping her daughter Jennifer off at Ball State. Here's Pauline on the set of* Paint Along with Pauline. *Here's a screen-grab from the concert film* Gimme Shelter *where you can clearly see a wild-eyed Pawneean housewife wearing nothing but psychedelic body paint and snorting a line of cocaine off a Hell's Angel's sunglasses, as the Flying Burrito Brothers play at Altamont Speedway.*]

LK: She was on *Laugh-In*? [correction by way of long explanation deleted]

KZ: . . . the point is, Pauline got into some pretty hard-core stuff, in terms of partying and drugs. And in episode 11, she is tripping balls. Which explains the psychedelic sky dots.

LK: Oh my God! So . . . so, the flaming rocking horse with Joan of Arc's head?

KZ: Shrooms.

LK: The inside-out frog from episode 12? And the four-barreled happiness gun that shoots color-feelings?

KZ: Peyote.

LK: My God. So . . . this lost episode you found. Episode 14. The one that never aired.

KZ: I don't think you should watch it.

LK: I have to.

KZ: You don't want to see it, I promise you.

LK: Yes, I do.

KZ: No, you don't.

LK: I really do.

KZ: No, Ms. Knope. You do not.

[*This goes on for a while. Then:*]

KZ: [*grabbing DVD labeled "SAMIZDAT: DO NOT WATCH"*] Okay. Don't say I didn't warn you.

I cannot, in good conscience, tell you what I saw in episode 14. There are things best left unknown in this world, and whatever worlds may lie beyond our own. Also, I am not quite sure I could tell you if I tried. Mirrors within mirrors within mirrors within mirrors . . . acts between man, woman, and beast that are so wickedly vile, yet achingly beautiful, that you think you can hear a sliver of your soul flapping in the cruel wind like a fallen soldier's banner on some scarred battlefield . . . a corkscrew-shaped monkey with eight butts . . .

Some lost episodes are best left lost. And this one will not sully my memories of *Paint Along with Pauline*, which are nothing but happy, positive, and full of childlike wonder.

All that being said, I'm totally going to buy some Aliziran Crimson and try to paint that monkey.

POTATO STEVE by April Ludgate

My favorite part about living in Pawnee is the wide array of art and culture. Just kidding. That does not exist. But there is one guy that can't go without being mentioned. His name is Potato Steve. They call him that because he used to live on the streets and smoke pot out of a potato and then eat the potato as his dinner. So gross and awesome. He's like seventy now and no one really knows where he is, and there aren't even any pictures of him, but he's the coolest guy in town and you should know about him.

Photo unavailable.

He used to be a roadie for a ton of cool punk bands in the eighties. One summer he was touring with Iggy Pop and the tour bus stopped in Pawnee. The bus left without him and he ended up just never leaving. He wandered around town for years, drunkenly screaming at people about the lack of fresh potatoes in our grocery stores. Then, after being homeless for a while, he wound up sleeping in an abandoned building on Racine, which eventually he claimed with squatter's rights and turned into a record store. (It's now a Taco Bell/Pizza Hut/Taco Bell Express.)

Potato Steve's Classic Vinyl was the only cool place for like a billion miles in any direction. You could go there and see actual like interesting people who were actually interested in something other than fast food and being stupid. I loved it. He also started a recording studio in the back room, and for like six months Pawnee actually had some kind of cool music happening. Here is a list of just some of the local bands he produced: *Piss Pete, Barf Monkeys, Suck Market, The Pukes, The Vomit, Garfield Puke, Grundle Taint and the Bullimics, Vomit Vomit Vomit, The Dad from Family Circus's Vomit, Steel Barfnolias, Bob and Carol and Ted and Vomit, Puke Finger, Suburban Swimming Pool Filled with Barf.*

So, yeah, basically every cool band ever.

I had the privilege of meeting Potato Steve once. It was outside of a punk show I went to in a cemetery (Retch Finger).[137] I went up to him and told him how awesome I thought he was. I'll never forget what he said, because he didn't say anything. He just looked at me and hocked a loogie on the ground. And, for some reason, in that moment . . . that was the greatest thing he could have possibly done. He totally delivered.

Here's to you, Potato Steve. I hope you're somewhere amazing, making music that almost no one likes.

---

[137] Two of the guys from Puke Finger, the lead singer from Steel Barfnolias, and the triangle player from the Dad from Family Circus's Vomit formed a supergroup, Retch Finger. They were only together for like three days, but they ruled.

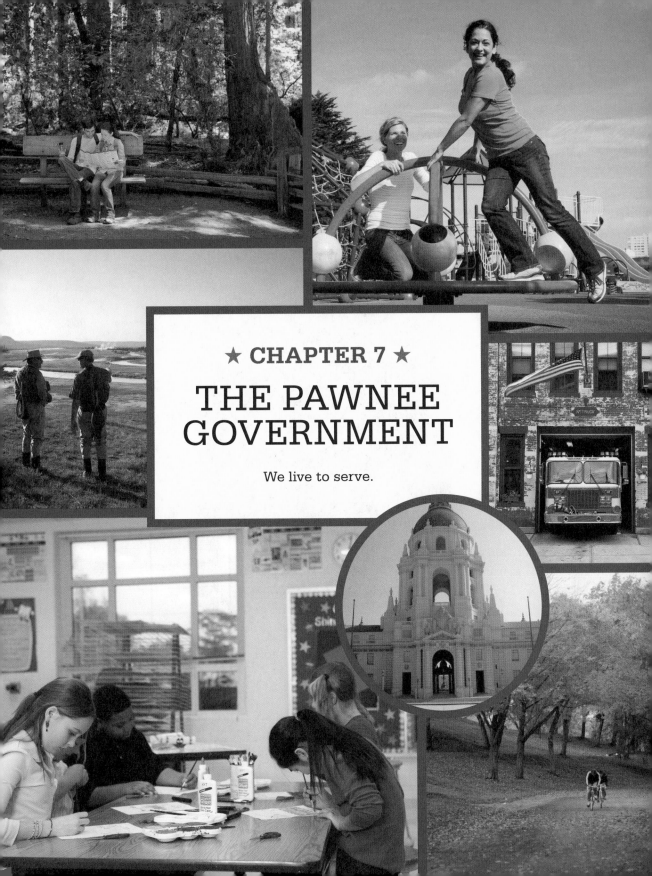

★ CHAPTER 7 ★

THE PAWNEE GOVERNMENT

We live to serve.

7

Your Tax Money at Work: The People of the Pawnee Government

The government of Pawnee is fairly standard in structure—a five-member elected city council, who work with (but do not report to) a mayor. His job—and I say "his" because Pawnee has never had a female mayor—is to be the public face of the government, listen to the people, and help the council figure out ways to improve the city. But really, the city manager's office does all the work, and the mayor just plays a lot of golf and gets his picture taken. Usually the pictures are out of focus, because he's literally sprinting back to the golf course.

Here are some of the men and women who have been charged with our public safety and well-being:

Chris Traeger, City Manager[138] In charge of the day-to-day operation of the government. Recently led massive government-wide "Health Initiative" that led to City Hall workers dropping a collective twelve hundred pounds. If you mention this fact to him, he will begin to weep so heavily (out of joy) that you will get embarrassed and have to walk away. He will not be embarrassed at all.

Benjamin Wyatt, Assistant City Manager Chris's right-hand man. When Ben was eighteen, he was elected mayor of his hometown, Partridge, Minnesota. He then

---

[138] Chris is technically still the temporary city manager. He was appointed to the position after former city manager Paul Iaresco had a massive heart attack, which required the rarely performed octuple bypass.

spent all of his town's money on an indoor winter sports complex he called "Ice Town." It was never finished and drove the city into bankruptcy.[139] Since then he has developed into an expert government finance advisor and has fixed the budgets of dozens of Indiana towns. One of the most competent, brilliant, and charming individuals you'll ever meet.[140] [141] [142]

Hugh Trumple, Police Chief Chief Trumple has served his city for more than thirty years. He is a man of few words. Once, legend has it, a woman approached him at a party and said, "Chief Trumple, I made a ten-dollar bet with my husband that I could get you to say more than two words." Chief Trumple replied: "Get the hell out of my face." Then he gave her ten bucks and walked off.

Marlene Griggs-Knope Director, County School Board Marlene has been in public service since 1975 and in that time has held just about every meaningful job in the area. "I stepped on a lot of heads to get where I am," she says, often, "and I'll step on a lot more before I'm through."[143] Full disclosure: Marlene is my mom, and I love her, despite quotes like that one.

Joe Fantringham, Director, Sewage Department Joe has made a career of, as he puts it, "living in the gutter." Famous around City Hall for his inappropriate jokes and easily prosecutable sexual harassment, he has served in Sewage since 1994. His proudest possession is his large white van with airbrushed Journey and Van Halen logos on the front and back windshields, respectively.

[139] Note from Ben Wyatt: Really? We have to bring this up again?

[140] Note from Tom Haverford: And a huge nerd. He once recommended a movie called *Cube*, which I started to watch, until I realized it was a *Canadian sci-fi movie*. Canadian sci-fi?! Have you ever in your entire life heard of something dorkier than Canadian sci-fi?

[141] Note from Ben Wyatt: *Cube* is awesome. Don't listen to him. Not so awesome is the sequel, *Cube 2: Hypercube*. Don't bother.

[142] Note from Tom Haverford: I won't.

[143] She's actually very sweet, if you get to know her, and if you don't care that much about politesse or cursing in mixed company.

Tammy Swanson, Library Director Tammy is a horrifying demon sent from the future to destroy all happiness. Her ex-husband Ron Swanson described talking to her as "staring into the eye of Satan's butthole." Despite that metaphor's lack of anatomical sense, it is 100 percent accurate.

Al Connor, Fire Chief Chief Connor is Pawnee's longest-tenured department head, having taken over the Fire Department at age twenty-nine, after everyone else quit due to lack of hoses. He is known for his easygoing manner and corny jokes, as well as for having that disease where you can't feel pain when exposed to extreme temperatures. So, "firefighter" was kind of a no-brainer, career choice–wise.

Harris Wittels & Brett Hull, Co-Directors, Animal Control Department These two geniuses took over control of the department when longtime director Eugene Dredge retired last year, presumably to spend more time with his bong. You would think that a town with the pest problems we have could find a competent person to execute this vital public service. We cannot. We have Harris and Brett.

Ron Swanson, Parks Department Director Ron Swanson needs no explanation.

Fun Facts . . .
About Some of Pawnee's Mayors and
City Councilmen and –Women Through History

Braxton Masonary

(Councilman 1892–1896, Mayor 1896–1904)

Mayor Masonary *never* said the word "good-bye." Family members claim that he would suddenly leave a room or sneak out a back door rather than utter that word. When the next mayor, Elias Waterstaff, took over his position, Mayor Masonary never formally said good-bye, and continued to show up at the mayor's office. For several awkward weeks there were two Pawnee mayors.

Emmet Plushgaurdin (Mayor 1864–1868)

Plushgaurdin was the tenth of fifteen children. His mother, Mavis Plushgaurdin, claimed, "I love all my children and I wish I could have fifteen more." Emmet's father, Tobias, left his wife because he was disappointed that she could not produce thirty children. Bonus fun fact: Plushgaurdin was also the first mayor to attend meetings.

Terp Haskins (Councilman 1959–1963; Mayor 1963–1966)

Haskins, the third tallest Pawnee mayor, went missing for six and a half weeks during his mayoral term. Just when most Pawneeans thought he'd never return or that he was dead, he showed up in the middle of a city council meeting, fully tanned, with his arm in a cast, holding a baby. To this day no one knows where he was for those six and a half weeks, or if the baby was his. When asked about it, Haskins would just laugh and say, "Crazy, right?"

Hugh Dupuis St. John (Councilman, 1936)

St. John was Pawnee's oldest city councilman, elected at the age of ninety-one. He loved bananas and was often heard to say, "I'm bananas about bananas!" He was found dead at his desk his second day in office.

Paula Hork (Councilwoman, 1971–1978)

Hork was the first female member of the Pawnee City Council. Sadly, that is the most interesting thing about her by a factor of about a thousand. I met her at a cocktail party late in her life, and she was so stultifyingly dull I literally forgot I was talking to a human being and put my hors d'oeuvre plate on her head.[144]

Reginald Jump (Councilman 1992–1996)

A firebrand of the ultraconservative wing of Pawnee's Republican Party, Jump campaigned feverishly against gay and lesbian rights. When the Bulge, Pawnee's first gay bar, opened in 1995, Jump would sometimes spend hours of his free time standing outside the door passing out leaflets urging the patrons to change their "lifestyles," offering his own assistance in private tutoring sessions. Jump also exclusively drank Campari and soda, and had Indiana's largest Marilyn Monroe memorabilia collection.[145]

---

[144] She was short, too—like four-foot-nine. So I suppose that's something kind of interesting about her.
[145] I'm not saying . . . I'm just saying.

William "Bill" Dexhart (Councilman 1996–present)

By far the most controversial figure in Pawnee City Council history, Dexhart has been embroiled in literally dozens of sex scandals. The most famous of these was when he claimed to be building houses with Habitat for Humanity but was actually having four-way sex in a cave in Brazil. He is now best known for his fiery, defiant press conferences, in which he always (a) admits his guilt while (b) simultaneously claiming to be the victim of a witch hunt. In fact, the last time he ran for office—successfully, I might add—his campaign slogan was "I have no plans to resign."

The Pawnee Parks Department: The Pride of Indiana

If you Google "Parks" and "best idea," you'll find links to some people who got stoned and went to Six Flags. But you'll also find a link to a wonderful Ken Burns documentary (*The National Parks: America's Best Idea*) about our national parks system. If you haven't watched all twelve hours of this amazing series, please put this book down and go do that, twice, and then come back. If you have, then you have some idea about how I feel about Pawnee's park system.

What is more beautiful, more democratic, more *American*, than a park? Men and women can come to these simple open spaces, meet each other, fall in love, fight, make up (but not make out, please), get married, have children (but not conceive children, please), and then take those children back to those same open spaces and watch their children play. It's like a vicious cycle, but awesome and positive.

At the risk of seeming hyperbolic, the Pawnee Parks Department is the greatest collection of amazing geniuses ever assembled in America. And I would like to take this moment to salute them, my coworkers, for their hard work and dedication to a cause I hold very dear.

In addition to the gems listed below, Pawnee has dozens of smaller tot-lots and green spaces that are absolutely worth visiting. Not to mention the many historical and recreation properties we help manage, or the actual Parks Department administrative offices themselves at City Hall, which in their own way are quite beautiful. So while you're here, please visit one of Pawnee's many beautiful public spaces. Because if you don't, honestly, I will be personally offended. I mean, in a way, I kind of put this whole book together so you would visit our parks, so, I mean, come on. You kind of owe it to me, a little.

Ramsett Park Our largest and most-visited park! Come see the statue of Mayor Percy, walk your dog by Pimental Creek, tour the Pawnee Zoo, drop in at the Community Center, use our countless walking and biking paths—there is literally so much to do in Ramsett Park you will get dizzy. I once spent every day for a month in Ramsett Park and never did the same thing twice. Granted, I was teaching a Community Center class called "30 Activities in 30 Days," and also granted, I got confused on Day 18 and repeated "Jog-etry," where we tried to jog and write poetry at the same time, but the fact remains: Ramsett Park is a bottomless fount of fun.

Harvey James Park Pawnee's number two "Most Beautiful Place," according to a 2010 survey of local residents—and it only came in second because of a prank write-in campaign led by some punky kids from the high school. (If you happen to see the survey, please do not try to visit "Mayor Gunderson's Taint." It's not a weirdly named park. It's just the sitting mayor's undercarriage.) The main feature is the massive Great Lawn, modeled on Frederick Law Olmsted's famous Sheep's Meadow in Central Park, in that they are both large fields.

Tucker Park Once a run-down nightmare that several members of the VFW said reminded them of the Korean DMZ, this park is one of my department's greatest successes. The 2009 Graffiti Removal Project was the first step on a reclamation project that has turned this war zone into a fun zone! Most of the CDC sample collection tanks are now gone, the possum cities have been razed and/or eliminated, and the 2011 budget surplus provided for new equipment and significant progress in pond de-sludging. Come see this Phoenix as it rises from the ashes! (Ignore the actual ashes—we had to burn quite a few hobo encampments.)

Lafayette Park A small park that straddles the town line between Pawnee and Eagleton, Lafayette Park was the site of the famous "Border War," in which they put up a fence overnight to keep us dirty Pawneeans off the precious Eagleton land. It is now the site of the extremely popular Pawnee Whiffle Ball League, which serves the dual purposes of providing free fun for children of all ages and shaming those rich Eagleton snobs. Every peal of laughter, every gesture of sportsmanship, every child's smile that results from our games is like a hot, serrated dagger being plunged into the soft underbelly of their miserable, corrupt, fat, jiggling bellies. So join today! (League runs May through August—sign up at the Parks Dept.)

Wamapokestone Park You may hear locals calling it "Wanna poke stoned," but Pawnee residents know it as one of the most romantic places in town. The park was established at the site of the shared grave of the nineteen-year-old Wamapoke bride named Hair-Like-Fire and the love of her life, Jedediah Smalls, who were secret lovers in 1848. Their story was like *Romeo and Juliet*, if Romeo and Juliet had been caught doing it, and Juliet's father had killed Romeo, and then Juliet had killed her dad, and then Juliet had jumped headfirst into the rock quarry instead of being hanged for patricide.

The main attraction of Wamapokestone will always be its medium-sized fountain. According to legend, if you hold the hand of your lover and throw a penny into the fountain, the two of you will be together forever. (If you throw trash into the fountain, you will be fined $50.) Visitors can also enjoy some shade under the famous grand oak "Love Tree," so named because of the carved initials found in the trunk. Some claim these are the names of five members of the "Reasonableism"[146] cult who committed ritual suicide in the park in 1976. Hopeless romantics agree, because it's true.

Circle Park Conceived in 1897, the park was so named because of its perfectly round shape. Over the years, eminent domain claims and rezoning have reshaped it into something closer to a giant letter "F." But the name lives on.

The Parks Department has done wonders with this space, as well—a recent initiative attempted to turn every discarded tire in the park into a tire swing, and the park now features an Indiana-record-setting 209 tire swings! So swing on over!

Pawnee Municipal Lot 48 This medium-sized lot is not a park—yet. But it is controlled by the government, and the Parks Department does have a development plan in place that will hopefully someday make it the site of the first new park in Pawnee in fifty years. Brought to my attention by astonishingly beautiful nurse/public health PR director Ann Perkins in 2009, Lot 48 has been the site of some truly memorable events, including the Pawnee "Santa's Village" Christmas Festival, the Summer Spectacular Freddy Spaghetti Concert, the Li'l Sebastian Memorial, and this time when we accidentally dumped a ton of dirt onto our friend Andy Dwyer's head while he was living in the pit that used to be there.[147] And I swear to God, no matter how bureaucratic and annoying it is, I am going to turn it into a real park if it kills me. Stay tuned!

The Median Along Route 37 It's not super-pretty, but due to an obscure city ordinance, it counts as a park. I can't really recommend you visit—there's nothing much to do but walk in a straight line and pick up trash. Which I do, every Saturday morning—come join me!

---

[146] See "Interview with a Reasonableist," Chapter 4.
[147] Note from Andy Dwyer: It totally didn't even hurt that bad.

The Man Behind the Murals

We have a saying down at Pawnee City Hall: "Come for the septic-system permit renewal—stay for the murals!"[148] All four floors of this beautiful building are lined with original eight-by-twelve works of art, telling stories of the most famous events in our town's history. The main force behind Pawnee's seventeenth most beloved tourist attraction[149] was a man named Arvid Burlinson.

Burlinson was born on the mean streets of New York in 1897. His parents were poor immigrants who performed backbreaking labor in a sweatshop seven days a week, scraping and saving every last bit of money they could so they could afford to send their son to an orphanage. Arvid's hardscrabble upbringing left him disenchanted with capitalism and the American political system. As an angry young man, he was particularly susceptible to socialism's messages of full employment and food and shelter for the lowest-born.[150] In the late 1920s, he fell in with a group of radical painters and muralists in New York's Greenwich Village. Burlinson's drawings appeared on the covers of influential leftist publications such as *Rise!*, *Unite!*, *March!*, and the less-influential *Amble!*, *Equivocate!*, and *Compromise!*

In 1932, at the height of the Great Depression, Nelson Rockefeller was looking for someone to paint a giant mural in the lobby of what is now 30 Rockefeller Plaza. Rockefeller asked Holger Cahill, the head of the WPA program that funded jobs for artists, for a name, and Cahill suggested Arvid Burlinson. But when Rockefeller approached him, Burlinson replied, "Work for you?! The devil of industry? Never!" and spat in Rockefeller's face. Rockefeller complained to Cahill, who remarked, "I swear to God, I am going to send that son of a bitch Burlinson somewhere so miserable, so far removed from the center of this culture, it'll take an archaeological dig to find him." So he sent Burlinson here! Which is totally insulting but probably true. But when he said that, Pawnee didn't have these beautiful murals!

---

[148] Actually, no one says this, but I've been thinking about formally submitting it to the Southern Indiana Office of Tourism and Development.

[149] According to a survey sponsored by the Southern Indiana Office of Tourism and Development in 2009. Number 16 was "United Skates of America," the roller rink that closed down in 1994. Number 18 was "Soldier Field." Which is in Chicago. People are idiots.

[150] Note from Ron Swanson: Leslie has allowed me the opportunity to add one footnote in this book, and I choose to do so here. Socialism is for morons and weaklings. That's all. Thank you for listening.

City Hall Murals

SPIRIT OF PAWNEE

I was asked specifically by certain people not to include this mural in this book. But the idea here is "Pawnee, warts and all," so I'm including it, even though *Spirit of Pawnee* is one giant, hairy, painful, drug-resistant wart.

The mural depicts a proposed 1915 railway line that was to connect Pawnee with the major shipping hubs that surrounded it (Chicago, Erie, Pittsburgh, etc). The artist, a delightful racist named Peter Thorbutte, was told to create an image that would express how this modern advancement would better the town. In his mind, this meant showing a steam train blasting past Chinese stereotypes who are laughing at the Native Americans who are being mowed down by the train while drunk on whiskey made by (naturally) the Irish, while the Irish folk (leprechauns, really) are yelled at by killjoy harpie suffragettes. Really, nobody looks good here.

Thorbutte's mural, sadly, was met with nothing but positive reviews. "It heralds a new dawn," wrote the *Pawnee Journal*, "when our town will be reclaimed by the people who by God's decree rightfully deserve it. It is also the most pictorially accurate representation of the Chinaman's visage we have ever seen."

The mural stands in City Hall to this day as a reminder of our sad history with foreign cultures, and as a testament to how far we have come in this great melting pot, and also because it turned out to be really expensive to replace it.[151]

[151] A few years ago, a contest was held to design a new mural to take its place, after *Spirit of Pawnee* was (understandably) vandalized for like the fifteenth time. My department banded together to create what I think might be the most confusing and cognitively dissonant piece of art in American history, which I truly love with all my heart, and which hangs to this day on the wall of the conference room in the Parks Department. Come see it!

THE TRIAL OF CHIEF WAMAPO (previous page)

This beautiful mural depicts the "trial" of Chief Wamapo, who was accused by local cavalrymen of "being Indian," which in 1877 was a crime punishable by death. The trial, as you can see, was not in any way "formal." Although Chief Wamapo did get the last laugh, as the cannon failed to go off on three successive attempts, at which point Cavalryman Cammerford (on the right) stuck his head into the barrel to see what was wrong, and got stuck, leading Cavalryman Turnbill (left) to attempt to get him free by lighting the cannon, at which point the cannon operated properly.[152]

PAWNEE ZOO

Although Pawnee is known far and wide for its hospitality, we had never, in the year 1935, had a Jewish visitor. An incendiary commingling of mistaken identity, extreme xenophobia, and dumbness led to the temporary incarceration of Rabbi Elon Heifetz, who was on his way from Chicago to New York when his car broke down. Unluckily for him, the first man to pass him on the road was zookeeper Albert Langman, who legitimately thought he had discovered a new species. Rabbi Heifetz was incredibly gracious and understanding about the whole thing, even eating some of the fish proffered by zoo staff once he determined that it was kosher.

[152] A painting depicting the grisly aftermath hangs in Turnbill Mansion (see p. 21), as Cavalryman Turnbill was the first of the Turnbill Clan to settle in Pawnee. Should you take my advice and visit historic Turnbill Mansion, however, I do not recommend you look at the painting, which is both poorly painted and existentially horrifying.

TRADING POST

Even after their severe mistreatment by Pawnee settlers, the Wamapoke attempted on multiple occasions to help their European guests adapt to life on the harsh Indiana plains. Here we see early settler Morgan Sackett (blue shirt) and his father Lawrence (white beard) selling a tribesman one of their family's extra babies.[153] The settlers would then use the cash for gambling and drinking, which during the cruel winter months was the best way to cope with the fact that they had ignored the Wamapoke's advice on how to properly grow and store food for the winter.

WEDDING AT TURNBILL MANSION

This mural depicts the unsanctioned 1867 marriage of Pawnee settler Emily Lagana to Chief Kuruk of the Wamapoke. The secret ceremony, presided over by the progressive Reverend Turnbill, was beautiful and moving. Then word got out, and the ceremony was a bloodbath.

SUNDAY BOXING

For a few years in the 1880s, Pawnee went through a period of relative lawlessness, as most of the sheriffs quit due to low pay and a lack of adequately impressive hats. In their absence, an amateur boxing club started up called the Pawnee Brawlers, who promised:

---

[153] The Wamapoke raised at least two hundred Caucasian settler children from 1831 to 1877, purchasing them from the white man and keeping them safe before releasing them back into society when they, the Wamapoke, were sure the white children could protect themselves against the poor decisions of their parents.

"No rules, jus' punchin'."[154] I like to think of this less as a harrowing display of the things humans will do to each other when there is no authority figure to stop them, and more like a kind of proto-feminist movement, since (as the mural clearly shows) women were welcome to participate. This mural shows Anna Beth Stevenson, a widowed mother of seven, in a championship bout against Reverend Cornelius Bradley, who at the time was both Pawnee Brawler Heavyweight Champion and also Mayor.[155] This mural was originally called *A Lively Fisting*, and was later changed, for obvious reasons.

City Hall: Our Very Own Temple

As the Pharoahs had their Pyramids, as Louis XIV had his palace at Versailles, so too do our local government employees have a temple: **Pawnee City Hall** (100 State Street). Built in 1904, it was made from 100 percent locally quarried Indiana limestone, which we stole from a quarry in Bloomington, because the limestone in our quarries was atypically weak and crumbly.

Many visitors to Pawnee marvel at the size and impressive nature of our city hall. "How is it so big and nice," they'll ask me, "when the town is kind of podunk and blah?" And to them I say, "First of all, go screw yourself. This town is awesome." Then I will calm down, and explain that at the turn of the century, as cities all over Indiana began to move into the electrical age, and commerce began to take off (thanks to expanding railroads and canals), Pawnee's city council commissioned a new city hall from renowned architect Daniel Bishop, ordering him to construct "a building that will stand the test of time, and show the world that Pawnee is the fulcrum on which Indiana's fortunes lie."[156] The council spared no expense, nor did Bishop, and the resulting building—a beautiful, towering monument to democracy—essentially bankrupted the town for thirty years.

"In some ways," says city councilman Douglass Howser, "we are still digging ourselves out from under that debt, as the maintenance and upkeep alone on this building are astronomical. The fact that a town of this size, and with this budget, has such a monstrously large and intricately designed city hall is frankly ridiculous. And I think it sends a confusing message to our citizens, when the building suggests a much more

---

[154] Quote from Pawnee resident Jervis Bonk, in *Broken Teeth, Broken Dreams: An Oral History of the Pawnee Brawlers* (University of Wyoming Press, 1944).

[155] I'd like to think Ms. Stevenson won this fight, but alas, history, and her headstone, show that she did not.

[156] From "What the Hell Is *That* Doing *There*?: Pawnee's City Hall and the Dangers of Architectural Over-Reach," *Architectural Review*, November 1988.

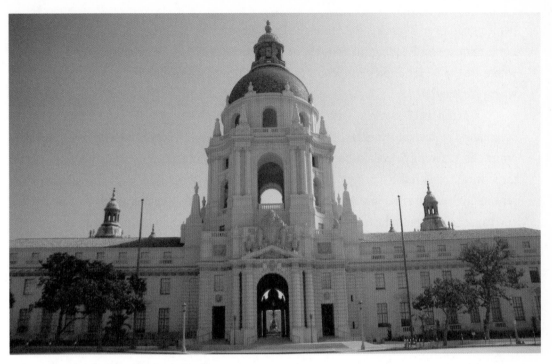

The most beautiful building in the world.

powerful and capable government than we actually have. It is quite beautiful, though." I agree, Councilman! (With that last part.)

Please come visit while you're here—although there are no "official" tours, if you drop by Parks and Rec on the first floor, any of our employees will be more than happy to give you a roughly three-hour walk-through of the building's main highlights. (Ask for **Leslie**, though, just to be safe.) One note of caution: do not under any circumstances visit **the fourth floor**. It is super freaky and scary. Divorce filings, small claims court, state-ordered drug testing . . . somehow both freezing cold *and* humid . . . there's a whole room on the fourth floor where they store knives that have been confiscated from people who went to the fourth floor intending to stab someone. Just stay away.

Other than that—stop on by!!!

Pawnee Public Schools—Educating the Future

In my opinion, Pawnee is home to some of the finest schools around. In the opinions of repeated state and federal assessments, they hover around the thirty-eighth percentile in overall quality. But while the U.S. Department of Education is quick to hand out C-minuses for Reading Instruction, or Math and Science, or Graduation Rates, I ask: where are the A's for Effort? For School Spirit? For Town Pride? Where are they? Really—where are they? Jerks.

The truth is, Pawnee's schools face the same challenges as every American community's: budget troubles, student apathy, bullying, rodent infestations, toxic emissions, cafeteria E. coli outbreaks, teacher/student affairs, teacher/student/principal three-ways, rumored hauntings, school board members who used to be in cults and repeatedly pressure the superintendent to include unusual religious tracts in science curriculae, school administrator suicide pacts, and so on. But the town is lucky to have some great people at the helm who have charted an exciting course toward excellence.[157] In the words of Pawnee school superintendent Dr. Benton Pringle, "Education is the passport to the future, for tomorrow belongs to those who plan for it today." Pringle is a dynamic leader with a PhD from the University of Phoenix in Inspirational Quotes. There are great things ahead for Pawnee Schools!

Pawnee Classrooms: Yesterday and Today.

ABOVE LEFT: Public education in Pawnee began in 1860, when its first one-room schoolhouse opened its doors to students from age three to fifty-five. Teachers were sparse—as were textbooks—and a lot of the instruction was given by local residents kind of "winging it." This photo, which dates from 1893, depicts a sixth grade class learning how Jesus defeated a T-Rex at Little Bighorn. ABOVE RIGHT: This photo, taken last year, shows just how far we have come since then, as students in a Pawnee Central High Earth Science class learn about how God makes dinosaur bones appear to be so old.

---

[157] You can read the whole plan, "Modest Gains by 2050: A Bold Vision for Slight Improvements at the Margins For Pawnee's Future," by Dr. Benton Pringle, Superintendent, Pawnee Schools, with Dr. Fran Merblin-Bloodworth, Ball State University, at pawneeschools.gov.

Pawnee's Sister Cities

What do Sarajevo, Krakow, Pyongyang, Kinshasa, and Boraqua, Venezuela, have in common? Yes, they are all sites of unimaginable tragedy, war, and/or ethnic cleansing. But more importantly, they are the official Sister Cities of Pawnee![158] I have never personally visited any of them, but recently we were graced by a delegation from the Parks Department of Boraqua. It didn't go great.

The visit began with an awkward greeting on the steps of City Hall, wherein the delegates requested prostitutes, and ended with me telling them Hugo Chavez was stupid and them storming off. Not the greatest moment in diplomacy history. But, in the spirit of municipal brotherhood and second chances, I have asked the head of their Parks Department, Raul Maldonado, to write a brief essay about his journey to our fair city. Before you read it, just know that (a) I have not edited this at all, and (b) he is a grade-A jackass.

My "Visit" to Pawnee, Indiana—Boraqua, Venezuela's Sister "City"
by Raul Alejandro Bastilla Pedro de Veloso de Maldonado,
Vice-Director Ejecutivo del Diputado del Departamento de Parques, L.G.V.

I have been all over the world representing the great nation of Venezuela. Wuhan, China. Minas, Uruguay. It is always myself and other esteemed members of the Departamento de Parques. Everywhere we are received, it is with many officials in uniform. A trumpet band always plays our Venezuelan National Parks Anthem as soon as we arrive. It is thirty minutes long and has many parts, and we all stand with much seriousness. We do this because we have pride. Cities everywhere (Wuhan, China, and Minas, Uruguay, for example) respect our pride. There is carpeting the whole way. Our shoes never touch anything that isn't a carpet. When we went to Minas, Uruguay, they carpeted the entire city. Imagine that in your thoughts right now.

Picture then what is was like for us to visit Pawnee in the United States. I sensed that something was wrong as soon as our plane landed. The workers driving around the runway were carrying on as if it were just any ordinary day.

---

[158] N.b. that these cities were all chosen well before the tragedies/wars/ethnic cleansings took place. Just bad luck.

Not one salute. No grand announcement was made over the loudspeakers. In fact, I did not even see any loudspeakers. I turned to my colleague Antonio and I said, "I don't see any loudspeakers here. Do you?" And I remember his answer as if it were yesterday. He said, "No." I said, "They must have hidden the loudspeakers as a grand surprise for us," and Antonio said, "Or maybe there are no loudspeakers at all." This was so horrible to think of, I just laughed. But it turned out that Antonio was right: not one lousy loudspeaker. This was a slap in the face that hurt me very badly.

As I walked through the airport, I noticed a tremendous absence of epaulettes on the uniforms of the workers. Was I in hell? Our servant got the suitcases and we waited for our limousines at the curb. But instead we were met with one van. A van for *all* of us to *share*. Like *animals*. Well, at least the motorcade was impressive—oh wait, THERE WAS NOT A MOTORCADE. I almost vomited.

I said to Antonio, "You know, we don't have to do this. If they aren't going to treat our visit seriously, maybe we should just send them a note saying we had to return to Boraqua on urgent Parks Department business." And he said, "I was thinking the same thing, but in the end it's probably more of a hassle to deal with press stuff and also rebooking the flights and everything." And I said, "Right, right. But man—they are being aggressively rude. One van!" And we laughed for a while. He is the funniest guy in the department.

This is an actual place in Pawnee. Can you believe it? I took a picture because I could not believe it.

Antonio Rivera-Fonseca, Minister of Small Fountains. Sometimes he makes fun of people right to their face without them even knowing it. At a gas station along the highway, he said to the lady, "This is the best coffee I have ever tasted. Surely you grow the beans right here on the premises." The way he did his face. I am still laughing.

The skyline of Pawnee looks like a pile of broken-down boxes behind a factory. You see it and you say to yourself, "We are clearly not there yet. This must be a war-torn slum that is ruled by drug dealers." But then the reality sets in, and a chill goes down your spine. "*This* is it?" The houses were all painted beige and white. There were barely any fountains or monorails. The restaurants serve horrifying fatty food I would not serve my dog, and for some reason they are all graphically represented by clowns of various sizes.

When I would set my eyes on something, I really thought someone would pop out from behind a bush and say, "Okay, this is the old sad version. But now look at the new version!" That did not happen at all. It was clear that Pawnee was not your Wuhan. Or Minas. The whole experience strengthened my admiration for the great Venezuelan president Hugo Chavez and all of his great accomplishments.

Our hosts were trying to be nice, and I sometimes feel bad for having been so judgmental, but then I remember things like having to eat low-quality chocolate in front of everyone and forcing a smile and thumbs-up. Very regretful.

I do not know how Pawnee became the sister city of Boraqua. Why us? I wish instead it was the France section at Epcot Center in Orlando, Florida. We saw videos of this place and it is just right. They have an authentic Eiffel Tower and cafés and everything you can imagine. It is very truly a Wuhan or Minas. Miami is also nice. Okay this is the end of this essay.

The "Aaaaawsome" Tale of the Pawnee School Board

We at the Parks Department feel like we're some of the luckiest people in the world.[159][160] We get paid to make this wonderful town even more amazing! But even we have to admit that there are some people in city government who might have it a weensey bit better. The eight-member Pawnee School Board not only helps mold young

---

[159] Note from April Ludgate: No, we don't.
[160] Note from Leslie: Yes, we do.

minds, they have nearly unlimited budgetary and rules-making power. Board members enjoy the use of city-paid cars and have all of their meetings catered by Outback Steakhouse.[161]

Pornographer/School Board Member Bert Aaschalegle, nee Schlaegle

Competition for these positions is fierce; every two years as many as fifty candidates appear on the ballot for only four contested seats. But the battle plan for campaigns has shifted dramatically since 1998, when an unknown candidate named David Aardsma won more than 96 percent of the vote, unseating six-term board member Frank Rutger. Confused political consultants soon realized that voters—who generally don't really pay attention—were just ticking off the first four boxes at the top of the (alphabetical) list. When notorious strip-club owner Bert Shlaegle won a seat two years later by legally changing his name to Bert Aaschlaegle, the "aarms" race was on.

Here are your current Pawnee School Board members, according to their seating chart at their regular table at Outback:

Kiersten Audette
Office manager, Pawnee Tool and Dye

Lenny Aamorrison
Out-of-work Nascar enthusiast

Maxine Afranklin
Homemaker

Phillip Bertrullio
CPA

Bert Aaschlaegle
Pornographer

Victor Aaaaaaaaaaa-aazerchenbach
Proprietor and editor, *Iron Cross* white supremacy newsletter

Randy Pilkins –
Gentleman farmer[162]

Derek Aaaaaaaaaaaaaa-aaaaaaaaaaaaaaaaaaaaa
Homeless

---

[161] Where, according to City Ordinance SB787-0004, the board is entitled to "All the Bloomin' Onions it can handle, bitches."

[162] Randy is just extremely popular.

Pawnee Animal Control

I have been asked by certain powers-that-be to include in this book essays and musings written by different members of our government—"For example," said the powers-that-be, "Animal Control." The idea being, let's let people get to know the hardworking members of our government so they can see how much we do for them every day. I told these certain powers-that-be, in no uncertain terms, that this was a terrible idea with respect to certain areas of our government, like, I don't know, Animal Control, who are a bunch of burned-out stoner morons.

But the powers-that-be were having none of it. So below is a harrowing, firsthand account of one Animal Control worker's experiences on the job. It is reprinted here in full, with no editing or commentary on my part. And if the result of this humiliating exercise is that the powers-that-be finally listen to me when I tell them that we need to throw a termite tent over the Animal Control building, drive all the morons out of there, and just start from scratch, well, I won't complain.

Animal Control Story
by Harris Wittels

Suppppp! I'm Harris from Animal Control, here to tell you about my most bananas animal control story. A lot of people think animal control is all fun and games, and it totally is. But, this one time, me and Brett had to catch this crazy snake and that was not fun or a game.

So, basically me and Brett are chillin, playin Call of Duty 3. This was before 4 came out. Obviously, we would have been playing that if it had been out. That game seriously owns. Speaking of, does anyone know how to get to the helicopter in Chernoble? I keep getting radiation every time I try. Email me at CritterCatcher69@PawneeAC.gov if you know what's up.

Sup?!

Anyways, it's our day off, but we get a call from our boss saying we HAVE to report to work. WTF, right? Not to mention, we were straight up cheebin on my new 3-foot binger that I got from this binger store down the street that's owned by these Persian dudes. So, we are baked like Lays (coincidentally, we were eating Lays at the time), in no condition to go to work, and we get called in to catch a snake! A SNAKE! On my top 10 list of the things I don't want to do whilst ripped on chronic, numbers 1–8 are catching a snake (9 is going to the dentist and 10 is CATCHING A F#***^%G SNAKE!!). And this is no ordinary snake. It was huge and venomous—one of those Copperhems or whatever. I thought they were only in, like, Brazil or something. Apparently not.

So, me and Brett go to the building with our little grabber sticks and our, basically, pillowcases. There we are, creepin around this building like that hotel scene in *Ghostbusters*. Such an awesome part of the movie. When he tries to blast Slimer and misses and gets slimed. I lose it every time! You gotta watch that movie blazed. So good.

Okay, so we are going through the whole thing and we can't find the snake anywhere. Then, I look out the window, and suddenly I am face to face with the thing (the snake)! It was so scary, dude! You don't know what it's like to be afraid of a snake until you've looked into the eyes of a snake. So I basically scream in shock cause I'm so freaked, but I don't think snakes can hear, so it just chilled luckily. But I froze and Brett was like, "Dude, what's up?" and I was like, "It's out here, man." And he started laughing. And I was like, shut up. Then he shuts up. Then he comes up with the idea that he should go to the floor above so he can do an "aerial strike" (once again, we were playing a lot of Call of Duty at the time). Meanwhile, I don't want to move because these things get scared at sudden movements and stuff. So, I am still face to face with this thing, like whispering to it stuff about the weather and smiling at it, just anything to put it at ease.

So, Brett goes upstairs and on the count of three he's going to grab the snake as I quickly get back inside the window I'm hanging out of. So, he counts to three and grabs it, and I get back inside but he drops it! Like two stories! And all the apartment tenants are standing down there watching and it just lands right amidst all of them! So it is pure chaos. People are running around screaming. Luckily the snake was as scared as the people were and so off it slithers into the woods.

Point being, the snake is still out there and if you see it please email me at CritterCatcher69@PawneeAC.gov.

Thanks for listening!

Day Trip: Pawnee Zoo
(Entrance on Howell Dr., adjacent to Ramsett Park)

The idea of a Pawnee Zoo was introduced by a professor of Zoology at Indiana State named Crawson B. Salt. After news reached Pawnee that New York City planned to build a zoo, Salt gave an impassioned speech to the city council, and the race to have America's greatest zoo began! New York opened the Bronx Zoo in 1899, and just twenty-six years later, Pawnee began construction.

In the early days of the Pawnee Zoo, most of the exhibits were simply animals on loan from local farms—chickens, pigs, and cows. Many of the cages were just filled with corn stalks and tractor parts. After falling into financial trouble, the zoo then began to sell the animals to their visitors, which led to an odd period in the zoo's history when it was essentially just a butcher shop.

We're working on getting better animals.

The idea was to show off animals from all over the world, but most of the "geographic" installations were based on conjecture. The Iceland exhibit, for example, consisted of a dog wearing mittens. In its third year of existence, due to an unfortunate series of circumstances, the Pawnee Zoo briefly included an older Jewish man as an exhibit.[163] The exhibit caused quite a scandal, because after it was explained to the zookeepers that the man was not a rare foreign animal and he was released, those with advance tickets were not given a refund.

The zoo has been continuously operated since 1930, except for two days in 1995, when it was shut down after the release of the film *Jumanji* caused citywide panic over animals taking over Pawnee. It really is a must-see. Be sure to visit both Fairway Frank, the legendary possum who terrorized Pawnee Municipal Golf Course until he was nabbed in a daring nabbing expedition, and the site of Tux and Flipper's wedding, which to this day remains the cutest gay penguin wedding in Pawnee history.

[163] See mural, page 168.

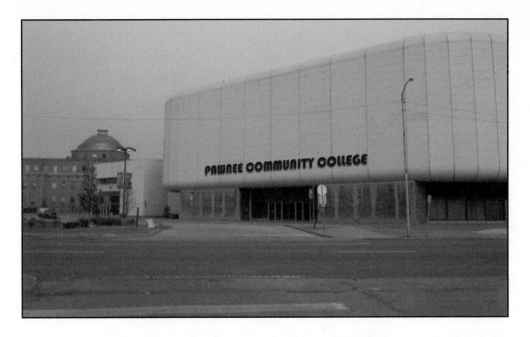

Pawnee Community College:
An Insider's Perspective

by April Ludgate

Leslie asked me to write a "comprehensive dissertation-cum-socio-historical-analysis of one of Pawnee's greatest institutes of higher learning," and I was like "what?" and she was like "write about your school," and I was like "no way," and she was like "please?" and I was like "no," and then she said I could take Friday off to write it and I was like "tell me exactly what to write so I can just type it and maybe I'll think about it," and she was like "no," so I was like "okay, then no," and then she was like "I'll give you suggested subject headings to create a structural template and also a coupon for a free hamburger-burrito at that hamburger-burrito place Andy likes," and I was like "fine." So here it is.

HISTORY I don't know anything about the history of this stupid college. I didn't even really want to go here. I take one class a semester to keep my parents happy. I don't even know when I'm going to graduate. It could be tomorrow, it could be never. Here, let me look at the website and see if it says anything that I can just copy and paste. No, that's too much trouble. Instead, I'm just going to read this horrible gossip blog. Oh look, two stupid people broke up. I hate them.

Here's the history of me going to PCC: I wrote my name down on an application and unfortunately I got in, because they're not allowed to reject anyone. I took some classes with morons, taught by other, slightly older morons. The end.[164]

CAMPUS Campus is gross. It has trees and buildings and cars. The best part of the campus is that there's lots of places to hide and then jump out and scare people. Also, I do this thing where I hide bags of liquids in different places and hope they explode on someone stupid. Here is a list of those places and the color of the liquid:

> Under a bench in the cafeteria (red)
>
> Inside a saxophone in the band room (black)
>
> In the dumb history teacher's jacket pocket (white)
>
> Under most cars (red)
>
> In the office desk of this professor who acts like she's all smart but actually
>
> > she sucks (white powder)[165]

FACULTY I had this one teacher who was really happy all the time and no matter how messed up I was she was always so nice and it drove me insane thinking about how she could always be so happy—like, literally insane, like I went to the hospital and everything (I didn't really, but I threatened to). I called her from my house and told her that I almost had to go to the hospital because of how crazy she made me and that I totally blamed her, and then when I went back to her class it turned out that *she* was in the hospital for real.

---

[164] Another thing April could have written: PCC was founded by the Newport family in 1965, after James Newport, the theoretical heir to the Sweetums fortune, was rejected from every single college to which he applied, despite Nick Newport, Sr.'s transparent promises of gobs of money (he allegedly sent $5,000 in cash along with each of James's two-hundred-plus applications). James eventually failed out after one semester, despite the fact that the courses were basically Jeopardy categories that were specifically designed to be easy for him: "The History of Sweetums," "People Named James," "The Influence of Batman on Modern Lunchbox Design," etc. Today, PCC has more than two thousand regular and part-time students, including our own April Ludgate, who is a lovely and intelligent twenty-two-year-old lady who I hope one day recognizes that my constant urgings for her to take herself more seriously—c.f. my request that she write this essay—will pay off in the long run.

[165] Another thing April could have written: occupying more than fifty acres in the northwest section of town, the PCC campus features modern buildings, the excellent Arthur Tellenson Student Activity Center, and the renowned Pawnee Child Development Center. (BTW, I am putting all of this in footnotes because I don't want to discourage April by not printing what she wrote, despite its complete lack of serious content. I think she's always kind of looking for people to not believe in her, which will reinforce her cynical, walled-up approach to life, you know?)

So I went and visited her or whatever and I was being really nice and then she was mean to me. And I was like: *finally*. Now we're friends.[166]

ACADEMICS I hate that classes give you grades but you don't get to give them grades. I'm the best at giving things grades. Watch:

Math: F	Work: F
English: F	Things: F
History: F	April: C
All Other Classes: F	April's Grade-Giving Skills: A[167]
School in General: F	

ACTIVITIES Uch, god, how many categories are there on this thing? This is the worst.

The number one activity at PCC is walking around with your mouth open like a moron like, "Duh, duh, I go to PCC, duh." I think there's a school newspaper.[168]

ATHLETICS Now I'm just going to type what I'm saying out loud.

April: Andy, what should I write for this part? It says "Athletics."

Andy: Write "PCC football kicks ass!"[169]

---

[166] Another thing April could have written: the PCC faculty are known statewide for their top-line research, teaching abilities, and accessibility. Indeed, PCC was ranked twenty-eighth in the Top 100 Community College Faculties in the 2003 *U.S. News and World Report* college issue. (In a way, this story that April tells reinforces my belief that the key to unlocking her potential is persistence. Calling her bluff. This teacher, whoever she is, was getting nowhere by kowtowing to April's poor behavior, but once she stood up for herself and drew a line in the sand, she seemed to earn April's respect. That is my plan, too. Of course, there's also the possibility that the entire story was made up. April also tends to lie a lot, just to mess with people.)

[167] Another thing April could have written: PCC offers hundreds of courses in everything from Math and Science to Liberal Arts, from Computer Programming to Philosophy. (I encouraged April to take her recent course load Pass/Fail, because I don't think letter grades and their psychologically loaded hierarchical nature are a good structure for her. I feel that people like April will try harder, and thrive, if they don't feel they are being judged by an institution, which to them (i.e., to April) represent a cold, impersonal value-designation mechanism. When I suggested she take the courses Pass/Fail, she in turn suggested that she drop out entirely and join a biker gang, so I backed off.)

[168] Another thing April could have written: PCC offers literally hundreds of activities, clubs, and societies, which are free and open to all students. The school newspaper is called the *PCC Weekly*. (I feel as though my little experiment to get April to engage is not working.)

[169] There is no PCC football team. There are a lot of intramural sports. (This is depressing. April is bailing on this, right before my eyes.)

LIBRARIES AND MUSEUMS Pass.

RESEARCH No.

ALUMNI Dr. Dre, Nixon

DEMOGRAPHICS Pawnee Community College is 100 percent African-American.[170]

SUMMARY Well, there you have it. A complete look at PCC, one of the dumbest places to spend your time in this dumb town. Whatever. All in all, actually, it's not bad. The schedule is really flexible, which I like, since I have to take classes at night, and it does provide the chance for a lot of people to finish school who otherwise might just like drop out and become weirdo drifters or something. If you're looking for a way to continue your education, you can do a lot worse than PCC. I don't really hate it.[171]

Just kidding, I do hate it.[172]

---

[170] There are libraries and museums, as well as great research facilities, neither Dr. Dre nor Richard M. Nixon went to PCC, and PCC has an ethnically diverse student body. And I have yet to find a way to break through with April.

[171] There it is. Success, in the form of one tiny glimmer of sincerity. I knew persistence would pay off.

[172] You're not fooling anyone, April.

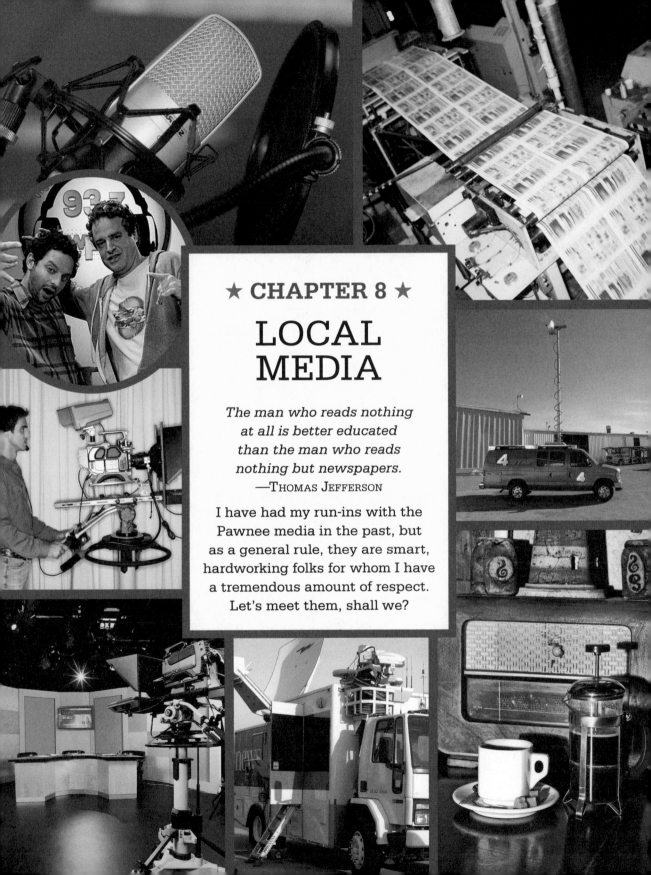

★ CHAPTER 8 ★

LOCAL MEDIA

*The man who reads nothing
at all is better educated
than the man who reads
nothing but newspapers.*
—THOMAS JEFFERSON

I have had my run-ins with the
Pawnee media in the past, but
as a general rule, they are smart,
hardworking folks for whom I have
a tremendous amount of respect.
Let's meet them, shall we?

8

WPWN: The Pioneering Sounds of Pawnee's First Radio Station

On November 2, 1920, families gathered in their living rooms, turned on an incredible new device, and listened closely to the sound of the future. As if by magic, a voice emanated from somewhere deep within the wonderful machine, and told the rapt audience that one Warren G. Harding would be leading America as it entered a new era: the Age of Radio. Nineteen years later, Pawnee got its first radio station.

WPWN is still going strong. So kick back, click on your radio, and tune in to 630 on your AM dial for Pawnee's seventeen-hour-a-day[173] news/talk station. Or turn to its FM counterpart, SWEET 106.7, and crank up the top songs of the day![174] Then turn it down so you can concentrate on this brief time-line of major developments in the history of WPWN.

October 16, 1938 The FCC grants a broadcast license to local dentist Paul W. Nermill. WPWN starts broadcasting from Nermill's dental office. The first programs are mostly drilling and screaming.

April 28, 1939 "Dr. Paul" begins mixing in lectures on dental hygiene, and on the relationship between sugar consumption and tooth decay. Radio and toothpaste sales go through the roof all over Pawnee. Candy sales decline.

May 4, 1939 Sweetums buys WPWN. Paul Nermill is found dead in a ditch. A dozen Sweetums-brand candy bars are found stuffed in various orifices in his body. All of his teeth have been forcibly removed. A note is scrawled on his chest in his own blood,

---

[173] Since 2008, the other seven hours feature the same sixty-second ad for the Wamapoke Sun Casino and Tax-Free Cigarette Emporium on an endless loop. Sadly (for lovers of news and information), those seven hours are during prime morning and afternoon drive times. However, the ads are the top-rated programming in Pawnee.

[174] As well as, for seven hours per day, the same sixty-second ad for the Wamapoke Sun Casino and Tax-Free Cigarette Emporium on an endless loop.

reading: "Candy doesn't make you lose your teeth—wrenches do." A bloody wrench marked "Property of Sweetums, Inc." is found nearby. The case is closed after the police announce that they can't come up with any suspects or possible motives.

May 5, 1939 The *Pawnee Journal* announces a massive investigation of the murder of the popular "Dr. Paul."

May 6, 1939 Sweetums buys the *Pawnee Journal*. The investigation is replaced by a story about how candy corn improves eyesight in combat soldiers.

March 1940 Edward R. Murrow broadcasts from rooftops during the London Blitz. Pawneeans read about that years later in history textbooks. In March, they were busy listening to WPWN and tapping their feet to *The Sweetums Hit Parade!* hosted by Dr. Tom Sugarman, "Sugar Health Expert," and sponsored by Sweetums' Gold Crown Extra-Sweetened Tooth Powder.[175]

1943–1948 This five-year period is truly the "Golden Age" of radio plays. Pawneeans are introduced (albeit a good fifteen years after the rest of America) to the wonders of radio dramas, comedies, and soap operas. Among the most popular WPWN had to offer:

- *The Whisperer*: A serial about a mysterious crime solver who whispers a lot.
- *The Talker*: Following upon their success with *The Whisperer*, WPWN writers create a serial about a crime solver who speaks at a normal volume.
- *The Yeller*: You can probably figure this one out.
- *Life with the Torvaldsons*: A long-running sitcom about a typical Pawneean family as they navigate the ups and downs of life—weddings, births, first dates, and frequent deaths from industrial accidents and/or bites from rabid animals.
- *Little Orphan Fannie*: A serial about a plucky orphan girl adopted by the wealthy Daddy Battledollars. WPWN wins record ratings and loses a record copyright-infringement lawsuit.[176]
- *Hi, Gene!*: The Indiana Department of Public Health created this program after many state officials visiting Pawnee for the 1943 Harvest Festival became ill

---

[175] "The Sugary Buzz on Your Gums Means It's Working!"

[176] The suit was filed in federal court, and WPWN/Sweetums planned to challenge it vigorously. On the first day in court, the Honorable Judge Terrence Quinby strode into the court, banged his gavel, and announced that the case was so cut-and-dry that "a damn kangaroo could see" WPWN was guilty. Sweetums lawyers protested, so Judge Quinby actually brought a kangaroo into his courtroom and made a grand show of explaining to the kangaroo that WPWN writers were just taking *Little Orphan Annie* stories and changing tiny details before retaping them for their own use. The kangaroo mostly just stood there and looked scared, but Quinby's point was made, and WPWN settled for an undisclosed sum. I would love to tell you this is the origin of the term "kangaroo court," but it's not.

after shaking hands with the locals. *Hi, Gene!* mixed important health messages into wacky story lines about Gene Clean and his overly friendly next-door neighbor Dale Wipeyourbum.

■ *The Nightly News*: Pawneeans often did not understand that there was any distinction between radio plays and news broadcasts, resulting in a petition signed by nearly everyone in town imploring WPWN writers to "kill off that harpy Bess Truman." This, in turn, resulted in a brief period of martial law declared in Pawnee by the Secret Service.

May 1956 WPWN is sold to local insurance magnate Arnie Flebbins, after federal regulators noticed that Sweetums owned every radio and television station in Pawnee.

June 14, 1961 Flebbins's son, "Moondog" Marty Flebbins, takes to the air, playing hits from African-American artists like Chubby Checker and Little Richard. Rock and roll comes to Pawnee!

June 15, 1961 Rock and roll is banned in Pawnee when, virtually overnight, dozens of teenagers drop out of school, get pregnant, and injure themselves in switchblade fights and/or while drag racing. The ban would end two years later, when people finally got sick of listening to repeats of *Hi, Gene!* on an endless loop.

August 30, 1967 Flebbins starts WPWN FM, 106.7 on your FM dial, playing album sides and deep cuts from the era's seminal recording artists, like Jimi Hendrix, the Beatles, and Janis Joplin. The *Indianapolis Star* wrote that "those who want to hear the sound of these incredible times need to check out WPWN—a beacon of light in Indiana's cultural landscape. On behalf of all of your fellow Hoosiers, we thank you, Arnie Flebbins."

January 21, 1974 The first FM radio is purchased in Pawnee.

December 1981 Both WPWN stations are sold to a Chicago-based radio conglomerate. FM 106.7 is rebranded as "KISS 106." Casey Kasem's *American Top 40* program replaces Hugh Trumple, Sr.'s long-running *Pawnee's Top 4*.[177]

January 1988—WPWN AM introduces its instantly popular "Weather on the 10's" feature.

---

[177] This was one of the greatest moments of my young life. For seven months straight, Pawnee's Top 4 was (4) "Wildfire" by Michael Martin Murphy, (3) "Holly Jolly Christmas" by Burl Ives, (2) Hugh Trumple, Sr. drunkenly singing the bass part to the Barney Miller theme, and (1) the Indiana State Senior Choir singing "Beast of Burden." It was rough. Then, suddenly—40 songs!? I didn't know there *were* 40 songs.

February 1988 WPWN AM introduces its seemingly redundant "Weather Also on the 4's" feature.

March 1988 WPWN AM introduces its definitely redundant "Every-Minute Weather on the Every-Minute" feature.

May 1993 KISS 106 changes to an all-Swedish-pop format, based on the phenomenal sales of Ace of Base cassingles at the Pawnee Sam Goody.[178]

September 1997 KISS 106 goes to all-Chumbawamba format.

January 1, 2000 WPWN and KISS 106 cease broadcasting due to Y2K computer meltdown.

January 4, 2000 WPWN and KISS 106 return to the airwaves after an intern discovers that power to the transmitter had simply been unplugged during the stations' joint "Ring in the Millennium" New Year's office party.

2004–2011 WPWN introduces a series of programming innovations that give us their current programming clock. As the jingle goes: "WPWN! Pawnee's News and Information Leader! With Traffic on the 1's, 7's, and 9's. Weather on the 10's, 4's, and mixed in with the traffic on the 9's. Sports on the 2's, 8's, and every third 3. News headlines on the 5's, 3's, and back-to-back on the 2's, 3's, and 4's every other hour except during the 2 o'clock hour, when the 4's are kind of up for grabs!"

2006 Thanks to the Bush administration's newly relaxed FCC regulations about media monopolies, KISS 106 and WPWN 630 are once again purchased by Sweetums. WPWN is largely left alone, except for the addition of a large number of somewhat suspect medical-advice call-in shows whose hosts seem to recommend high-fructose corn syrup as a kind of magic panacea. There's also a *Loveline*-style romance call-in show called *Sweet on You*, whose host, Dr. Drew Pinsty, once suggested that a caller's ED could be due to a "caramel deficiency."

KISS 106 is renamed "SWEET 106." All staff members are laid off except for intern Danny Guntz, who gets $6.25 an hour to make sure no one unplugs anything. The station's program director is a computer program called Top-Hits Algorithm ver. 2.7, located on a server farm in Sweetums HQ.

---

[178] A 2002 assessment by the Indiana Department of Sanitation estimated that a full forty inches of the total height of Pawnee's Larry Joe Bird Municipal Landfill is owed to All That She Wants cassettes and CD singles.

The *Pawnee Journal:* Our *New York Times*

For more than a century, the *Pawnee Journal* has been as big a part of our morning routine as coffee and cleaning up our front yards after rodents rifle through our trash barrels overnight. The story of the *Journal* is itself worthy of the type of long, thoughtful profile that used to fill the paper's Sunday magazine, before it was replaced by *Parade* and a circular for a local bail bondsman. The paper's founder, Houghton "Huff" Maxwilder, though raised in an orphanage,[179] used his street smarts and self-taught intellectual prowess to become the personal secretary to the owner of Just Stumps, the Midwest's largest lucky rabbit's foot concern. His rise through the ranks of Pawnee's business community was swift, and in 1908 he founded the *Journal.*

Huff built an incredibly successful regional paper, widely touted as a model of journalistic excellence and known for its in-depth reporting and hard-hitting analysis. But that was then. In the spirit of the current, not-quite-as-serious-minded *Pawnee Journal,* I've decided to tell the paper's story in jaunty, easy-to-understand bullet points.[180]

- The first issue of the *Pawnee Journal* rolls off the printing press on **January 31, 1908**. Money is tight, so the *Journal* is printed on flattened corn husks, "just like the *Chicago Tribune.*" This is a bald-faced lie, but one that sells papers like crazy to the aspirational, poorly traveled Pawneeans.
- By **1910**, the *Journal* is printing on real paper. However, Maxwilder can only afford one page per issue, thus spawning the paper's famous motto: "All the News That Fits, We Print."[181]

---

[179] After Maxwilder's mother died in childbirth, his distraught father went on a two-week bender, drowning his sorrows (as so many Pawneeans did back then) in a brew made of pure mountain springwater, a sprig of freshly picked thyme, and a dozen melted Morphiyums candies he stole from his job at the Sweetums factory. Cyrus was found lying on the frozen winter ground, making "concrete angels," and wearing "one of those crazy candy smiles" that were so common in town before Sweetums cleaned up its act.

[180] I tried to interview Jonathan Maxwilder, Jr. (now seventy years old but still feisty; also, kind of handsy) about the way the contemporary *Journal* differs from its original incarnation, and he replied, in a lengthy voice-mail message: "If you really want to write about today's *Journal,* just puke up some substanceless drivel cobbled together from wire reports by an unskilled, poorly paid, poorly trained kid fresh out of college who means well enough but who doesn't know a damn thing about doing real journalism—not that there are any real journalists left there to teach the young'uns how to write, after all those layoffs. Then drum up some vapid 'editorial' that just repurposes party talking points and call it 'analysis,' all the while doing nothing to make sure that analysis is in any way shape or form in line with the opinions or values of the local community you're supposed to serve, because no one on the editorial board actually lives in that community, but instead they are all sitting in some office in Dallas working for some giant newspaper conglomerate who doesn't give a French Lick about Indiana. Hell, why run a story about any important issue facing this state when you can run some puff-piece B.S. about Charlie Sheen, or Jay Z, or Madam Goo Goo, or Justin Bieber? I am so goddamn sick and t—" and then the voice mail hit its time limit. So, there you go.

[181] For the paper's first decade, when this phrase was the literal truth, the motto was, technically, "All the News that Fi."

■ Noticing that Pawnee's poor education system is holding back sales, in 1917 the *Journal* launches an evening edition written at a first-grade reading level.[182] Here is the lead editorial for **November 5, 1917**:

The Pawnee Journal

NOVEMBER 5, 1917   VOL. XVI. No. 34   TWO CENTS

THE MAYOR IS BAD

The Mayor is bad. He steals money. He cheats you. Do not trust the bad man. Tell the bad man, "no." Say, "you go, bad man." Tomorrow, you go vote. Vote for the man "Sylvester Twimbly." He is the good man. Do not vote for the man "Caleb Kihnstoger." He is the bad man. Also you drink juice. Juice is happy for your tummy.

■ Despite the trying economic times, the *Journal* does brisk business after the stock market crash of **1929**. This is partly due to the paper's extensive coverage of FDR's response to the challenges of the Great Depression, and partly due to the fact that the *Journal* began printing on shoe-shaped paper, perfect for attaching to the feet of barefoot dust bowl hobos.

■ **May 6, 1939**—just days after announcing that the *Journal* would be launching a massive investigation into the murder of popular WPWN radio host Dr. Paul Nermill—in which the Sweetums Corporation was strongly suspected of playing a hand, owing to the fact that they didn't really try to hide the fact that they had played a hand—the *Journal* is purchased by Sweetums. Huff Maxwilder is retained as editor,

[182] The Journal's editors began to suspect that something was amiss when a human error led to the same edition being published every day for two weeks and no one complained.

but forced to print pro-Sweetums editorials every day for a year until everyone basically forgets Dr. Paul existed.

■ **December 8, 1941.** The *Pawnee Journal* issues one of its most famous front-pages:

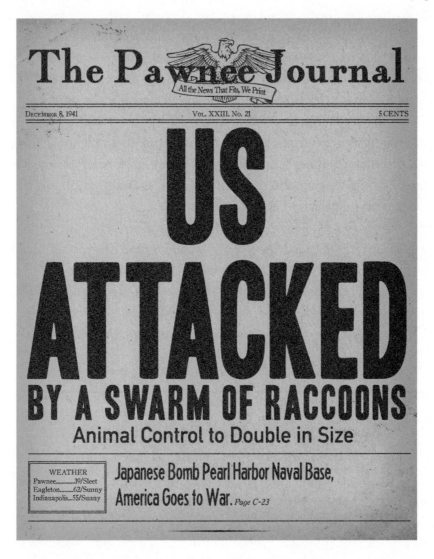

Of course, grammatically, it should have read: "WE'RE ATTACKED BY RACCOONS" or "RACCOONS ATTACK US" instead of "US ATTACKED," but that oversight notwithstanding, the story of the first Pawnee raccoon attack made the *Journal* a must-read for every citizen.

■**January 1946.** Sweetums, which had lost a fortune supporting the Axis powers in the war, is strapped for cash and sells the paper back to the Maxwilder family.

■ In **1966**, a movement begins to oust Indiana State University (at Pawnee) English professor Aaron Blanofsky, who was teaching Allen Ginsberg's *Howl* in his American Poetry seminar. Maxwilder, though by that time in his eighties, was a firm believer in free speech and expression, and he comes to Blanofsky's defense in a series of elegantly crafted editorials about the dangers of provinciality. Sales immediately plummet. Maxwilder resigns, leaving the paper in the hands of his son, Huff Maxwilder, Jr., who does a total one-eighty and calls for Blanofsky to be removed from the campus, "with a tank if necessary," and "sent back to Russia in a damned body bag" with "a copy of his Satanic hippie book" torn into pieces and "jammed down his weeping sore of a mouth" until he is "stuffed to the gills with his own festering, profane, Communist bullhonkey." Sales increase.

■ Maxwilder Jr. turns out not to have a great head for journalism, and he also turns out to like cocaine a lot, and after a few years he turns the reins over to his nephew Jonathan Maxwilder. A recent graduate of Columbia's prestigious School of Journalism, Jon immediately launches an investigation into systemic corruption at Sweetums. Things come to a head on **November 9, 1975**, with this editorial:

| EDITORIALS |

Sweetums' Sour History in Vietnam

YESTERDAY afternoon on Capitol Hill, the good name of Pawnee was dragged through the mud yet again. Sweetums C.E.O. Nick Newport was evasive, ornery, incoherent, and frequently downright embarrassing when questioned by House Veterans' Affairs Committee Chairman, Indiana's own Vance Hartke. Time and again, despite overwhelming photographic evidence, expert testimony, heartbreaking personal accounts, and audio tapes in which Mr. Newport is clearly heard saying, "What's a little cancer and hor-rifying birth defects when you're talking about Chinamen?" the Sweetums C.E.O. denied that Agent Red #5, the controversial defoliant made from the same red dye used in several Sweetums' products, caused cancer and horrifying birth defects among the Vietnamese. His repeated statement that "You can't spell 'sweet freedom' without Sweetums," was utterly nonsensical on every level. The editorial board of this paper will not rest until Mr. Newport is brought to justice and the Sweetums company is finally rid of its detestable founding family.

And here's the lead editorial from **November 10, 1975**, the morning after Sweetums Confectionary Corp., no longer strapped for cash, repurchased the *Pawnee Journal.*

| EDITORIALS |

You Can't Spell "Sweet Freedom" Without Sweetums

ONCE AGAIN, Sweetums C.E.O. Nick Newport cut a dashing figure on Capitol Hill as he charmed Washington's powerbrokers and the nation with his sharp wit and sparkling eloquence. The man and the company he leads are truly the pride of Pawnee. Might we also add that their products are among the most delicious things we've ever put in our mouths. With the Christmas shopping season just around the corner, we'll be dedicating this space each day for the next several weeks to highlight a different Sweetums treat to inspire the Santa and Mrs. Clauses out there who are looking for something special for Johnny and Jane's stocking this year. Long live Nick Newport. Long live Sweetums.

- **May 1977.** The *Journal* introduces its long-running comic *Pete O'Gold*. The strip followed the wacky adventures of Pete, an adorable member of a tribe of tiny leprechauns who live inside cavities and dole out luck to candy lovers.
- **February 1979.** Sweetums purchases its only local competitor, the *Pawnee Evening Bulletin*. It then goes on to purchase several other papers in surrounding communities. The *Pawnee Journal-Bulletin-Gazette-Times-Courant-Globe-Herald-Chronicle-Times-Tribune-Picayune-Times* is published from 1979 until 1983, when an ink shortage causes the publisher to shorten the name back to the *Pawnee Journal*.
- **March 1982.** The paper rolls out its beloved horoscope section, written by local astrologer Madame Delphinia Von Crystalina, Siren of Cassiopea (née Craig Degrabedian, of Degrabedian Electrical Supply).
- In **1983**, under pressure from morality watchdog group the Society for Family Stability Foundation, the paper cancels its beloved horoscope section. The SFFSF is widely known for its campaigns against anything it deems to be amoral or "heathen." Here, oddly enough, the focus was entirely on the Gemini zodiac sign, as the group believes twins are "unnatural."

- **1987.** Reporter John Woestednick wins the Pulitzer Prize for Investigative Journalism, for his outstanding reporting on systemic corruption at prisons and, in turn, proving an innocent man was falsely imprisoned for murder. His stories are printed in the pages of the *Philadelphia Inquirer* and noted in the *Pawnee Journal's* "Sweetums Presents: Bite-Sized, Candybar-Sized News from 'Round the Nation" info-graphic.

- **1993.** The *Pawnee Journal* rolls out its first full-color front page. Subscribers are so wowed that they don't notice the paper has simultaneously eliminated its World News, Sunday Magazine, Issues and Ideas, and Business sections, as well as two thirds of its editorial staff.

- **June 1997.** The groundbreaking writing of *Journal* restaurant reviewer Tripp Skermish grabs the attention of the prestigious *Columbia Journalism Review*! They call him "Pawnee, Indiana's celebrity reviewer" and include quotes from several local restauranteurs who claim positive Skermish reviews had them flooded with first-time patrons. The paper also notes: "Cultivating his celebrity and eschewing the age-old reviewer's practice of attempted anonymity, Skermish is lavished with so much attention, so many 'on-the-house' drinks and 'off-the-menu' specials, so many table-side visitations from chefs, that it's no surprise each restaurant gets his full—and anatomically questionable—'Five Thumbs Up.'" As an example, the *Review* quotes Skermish's review of the then-new Ray's Sandwiches as featuring "an absolutely scrumptious platter featuring toasted bread with a stack of several hundred-dollar bills."

- **August 1999.** The *Journal* goes digital, as PawneeJournal.com is born! Newspaper subscriptions drop 83 percent in the next six months.

- **February 2000.** Newspaper subscriptions rebound 63 percent the day after PawneeJournal.com puts up a pay-wall for its popular "Cats Who Look Like Dogs" feature.

- **2004.** Sweetums sells a minority stake in the *Pawnee Journal*, including day-to-day operational control, to FreedomMedia, a newspaper conglomerate in Dallas, Texas. They give us the paper we have today: 8 percent smaller, 43 percent thinner, 90 percent less local, three times as expensive, and nearly entirely see-through . . . but still 100 percent Pawnee!

JOAN CALLAMEZZO

Joan Callamezzo (born March 17, 19??) came to Pawnee in 1996 by way of Gary, Indiana. The daughter of Mason Owen Stephens, a former Broadway dancer and owner of the famed Footlights Dance Studio in Gary, Joan always loved to dance. She and her father made headlines in the summer of 1978 when they performed a modern pas de deux called *The Apple Tree* at the Indiana Arts Festival. Reviews were mixed, with some calling it, "perverse . . . " and "strangely anti-family."[183]

Joan on the set of Pawnee Today.

Joan's teen years were fraught with tragedy. Her mom, Janine, known for her massive collection of exotic lawn statuaries, passed away in 1980. The tragedy occurred following a party Mason threw for his "business partner," Peter, who was almost certainly more than just a business partner, based on the facts that the two men often vacationed together, wore matching clothes, and were once caught by Janine having digital sex in the family's faux-wood-paneled rec room. After the sexually charged party, during which an intoxicated Janine destroyed a cake Mason had made especially for Peter in the shape of the trolley car from *Meet Me in St. Louis*, Janine overdosed on prescription pills. She was discovered in her yard clutching a concrete nativity sheep. These years were traumatic ones for Joan, but she lost herself in her dancing, experiencing it as a sort of escape. And she was about to get her big break.

While attending the University of Pittsburgh, Joan landed a small role in the smash hit movie *Flashdance*. She played a waitress at Mawby's Bar (the classy strip joint with the arty stripping) and can be seen in several scenes serving burgers in a tank top with no bra. She continued to audition for movie roles and scored small parts in other hit movies, such as *Weekend at Bernies*, *Look Who's Talking Too*, and *The Silence of the Lambs*, in all of which she played a dead body.

Joan's movie career took her all the way to Chicago, where she became an aerobics instructor. There she met Franzio Callamezzo, who (along with his brother Santino) owned the Body Factory Gym, where Joan was employed. In 1995, after a whirlwind courtship, Joan married Franzio in a small ceremony next to the Nautilus machines.

[183] Trisha Maquin, "Did Anybody Else See That Incestuous Freakshow at the Indiana Arts Festival Or Did I Hallucinate It?" Gary *Gazette* Op-Ed Page, July 18, 1978.

To learn about Joan's reign as Calumet High School's Homecoming Queen, see pages 763–772 of her self-published autobiography.

The Callamezzo brothers, looking to parlay their Body Factory mini-empire into other successes, began looking at small-market radio and television stations for purchase. This search led them all the way to Pawnee (and back to Joan's home state) when they purchased Pawnee's very own Channel 46.

Formerly owned by the Baptist Church, Channel 46's programming had been limited to Paul and Sally Melcher's organ recitals, their terrifying puppet show, and a weekly children's Bible story reading by Paul Melcher's cousin Billy, who had been badly burned in a chemical fire. Within six months, the Callamezzo brothers revitalized Channel 46's programming lineup with shows like *PM Pawnee*, *Sex Talk with Dr. Pearl*, and *The Word, With Perd*.[184] The Callamezzo brothers now had Channel 46's finger firmly planted on the pulse of Pawnee.

This expansion into showbiz delighted Joan, and she quickly became the host of her own fitness show. *The Burn Zone with Joan* premiered May 14, 1997, and was an immediate flop. Joan had failed to notice the literal explosion of obese citizens in town, thanks to the introduction of high-fructose corn syrup into the city's drinking water.[185] As such, workout shows were not super-popular. Joan's failure resulted in a tearful on-air breakdown during a twenty-four-count grapevine step-toe-step.

But Joan's voracious lust for the spotlight gave her the strength to soldier on. In July of 1997 she launched a new show, *Who's in*

For more on Joan's high school years, consult volumes 3 and 4 of her self-published autobiography.

[184] Following a lengthy legal battle with the Callamezzo brothers, television personality Perd Hapley lost creative rights to his name and show. Since then he has launched several new shows: *Everybody's Heard About the Perd; Perd? Absurd!; Perd, In Thirds* (an hour-long show featuring three twenty-minute-long interviews); *Revenge of the Perd; Hapley Ever After, with Perd Hapley; The Road to Perd-ition Movie Review Hour;* and finally *Ya Heard with Perd,* which currently airs on Pawnee's NBC affiliate, Channel 4.

[185] One of Sweetums' rare missteps. They were sued by a Pawnee long-distance-running enthusiast named William Meyers who, despite jogging twelve miles a day, had gained eighty pounds in six weeks thanks to his commitment to proper hydration, and were forced to back off.

the Kitchen with Joan? A hybrid talk-and-cooking show, *Who's in the Kitchen* launched Joan's career, thanks in large part to notorious Pawnee city councilman Bill Dexhart.

Dexhart appeared on the show's fifth episode to discuss the community center renovation and make his grandmother's dumplings, but Joan got so much more. During the last ten minutes of the program, in between bites of steaming dumpling, Joan slyly asked Dexhart to speak about the rumors of his extramarital affairs. The taste of his grandmother's dumplings combined with the entire bottle of white wine he consumed during the course of the show caused him to spill his guts out to Joan, admitting that indeed "he had a problem."[186]

The Dexhart Confession was a watershed moment for Joan. "I'd found my calling," she wrote. "Investigative journalism. I realized that it was time for me to take my place on the Mount Rushmore of female journalists, with Barbara Walters, Oprah and that's all I can think of. Just us three."[187]

On January 9, 1998, *Pawnee Today with Joan Callamezzo* premiered on Channel 46, and Joan pulled no punches. Armed with the motto "Tears Equal Truth," she grilled Pawnee powerbrokers and glitterati about their private lives, failures, and personal foibles, aiming to bring her guests to tearful, televised meltdowns. However, this ratings-grabbing technique began to fail her, as she soon found no one wanted to appear on *Pawnee Today.* A desperate second interview with Councilman Dexhart failed to recapture their old magic, though Dexhart did admit to another six extramarital affairs that had happened since the first interview.

It was then Joan realized: she needed to face herself. As she put it: "I was forced to ask myself, why am I obsessively punishing people with their own truths? Is it because I am afraid to report on my own story?"[188]

To read Joan's thoughts on this haircut, consult pages 187–188, 295, 417–483, 921–933, 1122–1123, and Appendix 5 of her self-published autobiography.

---

[186] "I love the ladies," a tearful Dexhart whimpered. "I love to love ladies. I love it so much." "I know you do, Councilman," said Joan. The whole thing was disgusting.

[187] Joan Callamezzo, *Achieving the Beyond: One Woman's Journey from a Bra-less Appearance in* Flashdance *to the Absolute Pinnacle of Her Profession* (self-published, 2007), pp. 122–124.

[188] Joan Callamezzo, *Achieving the Beyond: One Woman's Journey from a Bra-less Appearance in* Flashdance *to the Absolute Pinnacle of Her Profession* (self-published, 2007), pp. 542–543.

And report her own story she did. On March 15, 1998, Joan did a two-hour *Pawnee Today* special called "Callamezzo on Callamezzo." The special guest? Joan Callamezzo. Seated across from herself through the magic of television, Joan confronted Joan about the real pathology behind her "quest for the meltdown." Joan revealed that she was indeed having a meltdown of her own. She and Franzio were going through a bitter divorce and—bombshell!—she was leaving Franzio for his older brother, Santino. "That interview saved me," she would later write. "I needed Joan to tell Joan that Joan needed to leave Franzio."[189]

This news rocked Pawnee to its core. Later in the interview, she opened up completely about her affair with her brother-in-law, her workout obsessions, and her issues with her father. This amazingly brave two hours placed Joan squarely back in the hearts of her Pawnee viewers, and guests were once again clamoring to be on *Pawnee Today*. "It was, as they say, 'the turning point.'"[190]

With her honesty, wit, and sassy appeal, Joan continues to rule the cable access airwaves, and as each year goes by, she solidifies her role as Pawnee's most visible and influential citizen. In 2008 Joan did a tenth anniversary edition of *Joan on Joan* and claimed to have softened over the years. Reading aloud from her lengthy autobiography, she said, "I'm still a straight shooter, but now I don't always shoot to kill."[191] But those of us who watch her every day know for certain—she is as sharp as ever, and always on the hunt for a scandal.

---

[189] Joan Callamezzo, *Achieving the Beyond: One Woman's Journey from a Bra-less Appearance in* Flashdance *to the Absolute Pinnacle of Her Profession* (self-published, 2007), pp. 980–981.

[190] Joan Callamezzo, *Achieving the Beyond: One Woman's Journey from a Bra-less Appearance in* Flashdance *to the Absolute Pinnacle of Her Profession*, (self-published, 2007), p. 1346.

[191] Joan Callamezzo, *Achieving the Beyond: One Woman's Journey from a Bra-less Appearance in* Flashdance *to the Absolute Pinnacle of Her Profession* (self-published, 2007), pp. 1882–1883.

QUESTIONS FOR PERD HAPLEY
BY LESLIE KNOPE

Perd Hapley

*The local legend and Channel 4 newsman opens up about his
unusual name, his love of hamburgers, and the trappings of fame.*

**In addition to reporting the news for
Channel 4, you also host a weekly, in-
depth human interest magazine show,
Ya Heard, with Perd. What do you
like most about the longer format?**
I guess I'd like to answer that question
by saying this: it allows me to go more
in-depth with my guests.

**It's certainly increased your profile
here in town. Do you get recognized
a lot?**
The only way to respond to that, would
be to say, "Yes."

**You have a unique speaking style.
You seem to almost preface all of
your sentences with a sort of
"run-up" to the actual sentence.**
I'd like to reply by saying: I don't
know what you're talking about.

**Really? No one has ever pointed
that out?**
The thing about my answer
to that would be that it
would be "no."

**Okay. You're famous for loving
hamburgers. What do you think is
the best hamburger in town?**
I will have to think about that before I
answer, and now I have thought about
it, and now I will answer by saying that
I think the best hamburgers in town are
the ones that you buy at McDonald's
Restaurant.

**Where did the name "Perd" come
from?**
I will tell you a story that answers that
question: it was my mother's name.

Really?
There's a statement I am about to make
about that, and the statement is: yes, my
mother was named Perd.

**I didn't know "Perd" was
a woman's name.**
Well I'll counter that by
asking this: have you ever met
another man named Perd?

No.
There you go.

*Interview conducted,
edited, and
condensed
by Leslie Knope.*

Pawnee Sun

"We Shine All Over Pawnee"   **Still Only 50¢**

ONLY **50¢**

CHEAT-UMS

Nick Newport Sr. Steps Out With Mystery Woman

Exclusive Photos, Page 2

The *Pawnee Sun*:
Pawnee's Very Own Tabloid

In 2004, Nick Newport, Sr., the ninety-four-year-old multi-millionaire president of Sweetums, refused to let his youngest son, Cal, use the family jet to take his girlfriend scarf shopping in Buenos Aires. Cal was furious. He self-printed a sixteen-page circular airing all of his family's dirty laundry—the scandals, failed marriages, and affairs . . . the drug abuse, alcoholism, and unpleasant sexual proclivities of his parents, his six brothers and sisters, and many dozens of cousins, nephews, aunts, uncles, and family friends. This wild overreaction was, by a factor of like a million, the most exciting thing that had ever happened in Pawnee.

The reaction was stunning. The Newport family had long loomed large in Pawnee, thanks to their massive wealth, veil of silence, and ensconcement in Capthorne Manor, Pawnee's largest private residence. Located behind a tall, spiky, wrought-iron fence, Capthorne Manor makes the Addams Family house look like the balloon house from *Up*. Suddenly, thanks to one spoiled brat's temper tantrum, Pawnee residents had gotten a glimpse behind the curtain. And we wanted more.

Cal struck while the iron was hot, dipping into his trust fund and founding the Pawnee *Sun*—a tabloid newspaper devoted to the scandalous underbelly of Pawnee society. Really, though, the only family anyone cared to read scandalous news about was the Newports, so most issues are just about them.

One would think Cal would have been completely ostracized, but Nick Newport, Sr., was so thrilled his son had an actual job, he wrote a letter *encouraging* members of his family to engage in more scandalous activity, in order to keep the *Sun* afloat. We know he did that because the *Sun* later printed that letter,[192] and in a head-swimmingly ironic turn of events, the issue of the *Sun* wherein the wealthiest man in town encouraged his family members—one of whom owned the tabloid—to continue their scandalous ways in order to sell more copies of the tabloid became the highest-selling issue of that tabloid.

---

[192] See Appendix 5: "Nick Newport's Letter to His Children."

Crazy Ira & The Douche:
93.7 FM's Bad Boys of Radio
by Jerry Gergich

Anyone who comes within fifty miles of Pawnee will be familiar with Crazy Ira and The Douche—Pawnee's most hilarious drive-time morning DJs. They're a little edgy, and a little "out there," but darn it if they are not hilarious. My wife Gayle doesn't find them funny at all, so I can only listen to them in the car when she's not around.

They really are "out there." Whether it's making strippers do math, putting exotic dancers in their famous "Spank Chair," or launching pranks on small business owners using their loyal army of local strippers, these guys are just downright edgy.

The unsung hero of the team is undoubtedly China Joe, their quick-on-the-draw sound effects guy, who always seems to add just the right audio rim shot to their hilarious escapades. It should be noted, out of sensitivity, that China Joe's real name is Doug Ng, and he is Vietnamese.

Over the years they have prank-called just about everyone in Pawnee, including, once, the head of the Parks and Rec Department, Ron Swanson! And I'll tell you what, it was a hoot. It happened when Gayle was in the car, and she made me change the channel, but later I got a tape and transcribed it. Be forewarned—it is pretty edgy, so don't read it unless you like things that are "out there"!

[*Ringing.*]

Ron Swanson: Speak.

Crazy Ira: [*old lady voice*] Yes, hello, is this Mr. Ron Swanson?

RS: Who's asking?

CI: My name is Beverly Fartsmuch, and I have a complaint about one of your parks.

RS: There is a public forum tomorrow. You can voice it there. Good day.

CI: No—wait!

[*Dial tone.*]

The Douche: He hung up! What an ass!

[*SFX: fart noise.*]

CI: I'm calling him back.

   [*Ringing.*]

RS: Speak.

CI: [*old lady voice*] Mr. Swanson, it's Beverly Fartsmuch again—

   [*Dial tone.*]

TD: What's with this guy? It's like, "Houston, we have a—[*fart noise*]."

CI: Unreal.

   [*SFX: long fart noise.*]

TD: Heh heh. Nice one, China Joe. That extended squirter always gets me.

CI: Should we just move on, or—

TD: No. Call him back. The Douche will take care of this.

   [*Ringing.*]

RS: Speak.

TD: Mr. Swanson, is it your policy to hang up on citizens who are calling to complain about your parks?

RS: Who's asking?

TD: I'll tell you who. This is Mayor Walter Gunderson! And I have never in my life—

   [*Dial tone.*]

   [*SFX: Pac-Man dying.*]

TD: Forget it, man. Let's just call someone else. I'm bummed now.

   [*SFX: long fart noise, followed by sound of something plopping into water, followed by man moaning, followed by second long fart noise.*]

TD/CI: [*laughter*]

CI: Classic.

   [END TRANSCRIPT]

Sweetums

IF YOU CAN'T BEAT 'EM...SWEETUMS!

Our high-fructose corn syrup is as pure and natural as a mountain stream

The way Mother Nature intended

Don't waste time at a less classy
Gentlemen's Club.
Instead, join us at one of our
highly-memorible nightly gatherings

100% DISCRETION
HIGH COVER EQUALS HIGH QUALITY
VALET
IMPECCABLE SERVICE
VIP CARDS
WALL TO WALL CARPETING
PLUSH VELVET SEATING

TALENT AND POISE

Refined women with elegant bodies
showcasing their most intimate selves

Fantasies...caresses...erotic music...
steak...gentlemen eating steak...in a
gentlemanly setting...baked potatoes

"The strippers you would want your
daughters to be, if for some reason they
had to become strippers."

New dessert item: poached pears

777 Howell Drive, Pawnee, IN 47998 812-555-0114

ATTENTION LADIES:
YOUR SEARCH ENDS NOW.

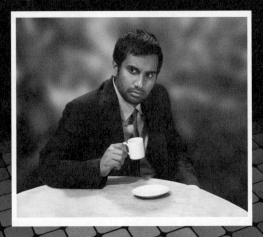

A real man is back on the market, and ready to be everything you want in a partner. I will treat you well. I will show you a great time. I will grab the reins and drive your romantic life straight to Heaven-on-Earth.

STATS:

SELF-MADE MAN
ENTREPENUER
VISIONARY
SENSITIVE LOVER
ATTENTIVE
ONCE DESCRIBED AS TYRESE MEETS CHANNING TATUM MEETS JADEN SMITH
TALL ENOUGH
FUNNY AS CHRIS TUCKER, COOL AS PACINO, SOFT TO THE TOUCH LIKE A BABY

Come fly away with me, to a place you've always wanted to be.

If you know where I live, as many of you do, the key is in a Drake CD cover under my welcome mat. Let yourself in, and we'll enjoy champagne, conversation, and "whatever the night brings us." And yes, I do love to cuddle.

Afterwards we could go see puppies at the pet store. Package deal. Whatever you want.

If I'm not home, just wait. I'll be there soon. Please don't steal anything.

Hey, Gay Pawnee!

AT THE ♥ BULGE, WE LOVE YOU JUST THE WAY YOU ARE...
AS LONG AS THE WAY YOU ARE IS TAN, RIPPED, AND WAXED.

DIFFERENT THEME NIGHTS EVERY NIGHT OF THE WEEK:

MEATY MAN MONDAYS
TWINK TUESDAYS
WAXED CHEST WEDNESDAYS
CHER THURSDAYS
FREAKY FRIDAYS
THE SATURDAY STEAM ROOM
SENSUOUS SUNDAZE

THE BULGE

1302 Runyard, Pawnee, IN 47998
812-555-0155

If you look at the ad on the opposite page, and it makes your body excited, you need to come see us.

The Society for Family Stability Foundation

WE CAN
CHANGE
YOU

snakehole
lounge

1088 Racine, Pawnee, IN
812-555-0114

Check our Twitter for drink specials, updated every minute

So dark, you can do anything

DJ BLUNTZ spinning ya into hysteria

Available for rent during the daytime for seminars, kids birthday parties or funerals

Our name is synonymous with feces!

988 Oak Park Avenue, Pawnee, IN 47998 812-555-0114

OUR APOLOGIES

To the Emerson Fencing company, for not recognizing that typo before this went to press. Their name is synonymous with FENCES, not FECES. We were pretty sure that's what they meant but we didn't want to change it without asking and Ken was off on a job, and we couldn't reach him. In any case, sorry, and they really do make high-quality fences. So, if you need a new fence, <u>urine</u> luck! [Again, sorry – we couldn't resist.]

Still Available

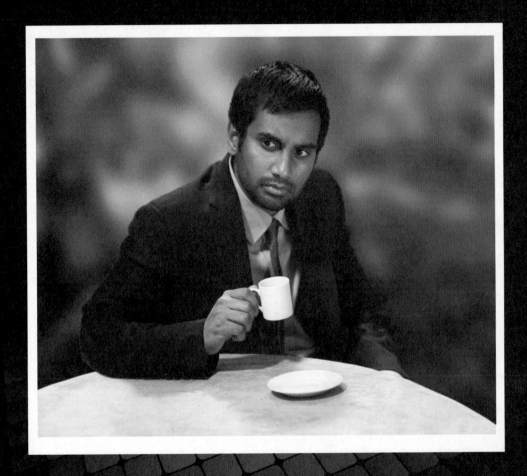

Appendix 1:
Racial & Ethnic Demographics

Like you, one of the ways I enjoy spending my time is poring over old census reports. It's like looking at a snapshot of a moment in history.

In 1900, Mayor Braxton Masonary declared that Pawnee would not participate in the federal census count, but instead would conduct its own survey of its citizens. Masonary was famously opposed to the federal government; in 1901, he successfully beat back repeated United States government efforts to make Pawnee one of the primary shipping hubs for the Midwest, which would've turned our town into an economic powerhouse. So, you know, thanks, Mayor Masonary. Less successful was his effort to secede from the Union and declare Pawnee the "Sovereign Kingdom of New Masonarica."

Masonary created the first Official Pawnee Census in an effort to check the federal government's work. So here's the Official Pawnee Census for the past 110 years and some earlier data I was able to dig up at the Town Records when I happened to be there in the middle of the night last week, during one of my infamous label maker binges.

2010 Official Pawnee Census
Caucasian/White 85.72%
African-American 8.97%
Hispanic, Latino, or Spanish Origin 2.44%
Native American 1.57%
Asian and Pacific Islander 1.10%
Other 0.02%

2000 Official Pawnee Census
White 87.35%
African-American 9.15%
Hispanic/Latino 1.80%
Native American 1.70%
Asian 1.67%
Other 0.03%

1990 Official Pawnee Census
White 88.15%
Black 9.35%
Indian 1.50%
Hispanish 0.75%
Grunge 0.25%

1980 Official Pawnee Census[193]

White 90.67%
Black. 9-ish%
Indian 27.35%
Mexican-y . . . . .L%
Other . . . . 1.1.72.35 ½ %

1970 Official Pawnee Census[194]

Whitey. 90.30%
Beautiful Black Kings and Queens. 8.27%
Oppressed Brothers and Sisters 1.43%

1960 Official Pawnee Census

White 90.00%
Colored. . . . . 8.00% (estimated)[195]
Mexican-Looking . . . . 2.00% (estimated)
The Takahashis . . . . 4 (total)

1950 Official Pawnee Census

Honest, Hardworking Americans 23.00%
Probable Reds 76.00%
Might-As-Well-Have-a-Hammer-and-
Sickle-on-Their-G-D-Foreheads 1.00%

1940 Official Pawnee Census

White 91.00%
Negro 5.33%
Red Indian 2.33%
Chinamen 1.33%

---

[193] Obviously suspect data here, owing to census taker Joseph Klipting being the first Pawneean to try smoking crack cocaine.

[194] 1970 report compiled by Doug X, founder and only member of the Pawnee Black Panther Party (not affiliated with the famous Black Panthers organization founded by Huey P. Newton and Bobby Seale). Doug X was a disaffected white teenager, born Douglass Hermann in 1955, to Diane and Norman Hermann, owners of Hermann's Landscaping. Doug has been known variously by his self-declared "authentic" Wamapoke name, "Strong as a Hundred Horses," by "Roberto Hinojosa" during his Sandinista phase, then, for almost twenty years, by "Ann-Marie Robideaux." After seeing *Avatar*, he briefly went by "Tsur Nar Zam Tsivo Sing Pali," which he claimed meant "Strong as a Hundred Horses" in Na'vi, but which was more likely just gibberish.

[195] The 1960 Census was conducted by Marlon Boddicker, deputy town manager 1958–1961 and world famous scaredy-cat. Wouldn't talk to African-Americans to conduct census. Also, wouldn't open the door to strangers. Or walk on rugs in socks during wintertime out of fear of electric shocks. Wuss.

1930 Official Pawnee Census*

Canceled Due to Stock Market Crash[196]

1920 Official Pawnee Census[197]

Nordic Aryan 13.25%
Nordic High Aryan 12.00%
Nordic Low Aryan 10.75%
Nordic Borderline Translucent Aryan 10.10%
Pauper (Circumstantial) 8.30%
Pauper (Hereditary) 7.60%
Classy 7.25%
Knock-kneed 2.75%
Soft-Chinned 3.75%
Dusky 2.80%
Smokey 1.70%
Swarthy 1.50%
Milk-Chocolaty 1.25%
Do-Able 1.25%
Hottentot 1.10%
Savage 1.00%
Feeble 0.90%
Hebrew 0.85%
Jug-eared 0.80%
Uppity 0.75%
Pants-Prone 0.66%
Schoolmarmish 0.60%
Randy 0.55%
Eagletonian 0.50%
Yellow 0.40%
Yeller 0.35%
Grayish 0.29%
Fancy 0.25%
Schmancy 0.10%
Genius 0.05%

[196] Census taker Harry Otway was struck and killed when Burt Freed drove his 1928 Model A through the plate glass window at Marvin Stock's Market and Haberdashery.

[197] 1920 Census conducted by noted "Race Scientist" and Eugenicist Dr. Filbert Crayton-Woont of the University of Indiana, whose book *The Tell-Tale Nostril Circumference: A Field Guide to Identifying the World's Races* was discredited as racist nonsense essentially at the very moment it was published.

1910 Official Pawnee Census*

*No Data Available (Lost in
Great Pawnee Fire of 1910)*

1900 Official Pawnee Census

White 91.00%
Red 2.75%
Yellow 2.25%
Black 1.75%
Halvesies 1.50%
Quadroon 0.75%
Octaroon 0.25%
Sexdecaroon 0.10%
Duotringinaroon 0.05%
Scary 0.02%

1882 Pawnee Factory Owner Assessment of the Workforce

People of All Ages Who Should
Be Working In Factories 100%
People of Any Age Who Shouldn't
Be Working in Factories 0%

1870 U.S. Cavalry Population Assessment

Americans 92.00%
Targets 8.00%

1841 U.S. Westward Expeditionary Mission Assessment

Christian 89.00%
Chattel 6.00%
Heathen 5.00%

1819 First Pawnee Unofficial Census

Us 79.27%
Them 20.73%

Appendix 2:
The Swanson Pyramid of Greatness

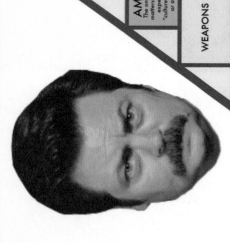

HONOR
If you need it defined, you don't have it.

AMERICA
The only country that matters. If you want to experience other "cultures," use an atlas or a ham radio.

BUFFETS
Whenever available. Choose quantity over quality.

WEAPONS

WOOD WORKING

WELFARE AVOIDANCE

TEAMWORK
Work together as if your life depended on it...IT DOES!

SELFISHNESS
Take what's yours.

HAIRCUTS
3 acceptable styles: High and Tight, Crew Cut & Buzz Cut.

GREATNESS ITSELF
The best revenge.

DISCIPLINE
The ability to repeat a boring thing over and over again.

ATTIRE
Shorts over 6" are capri pants. Shorts under 6" are European.

SELF-RELIANCE
Trust yourself.

SUSPICION
Do not trust anyone else.

SKIM MILK
That's right. It's on here twice. Avoid it.

COW PROTEIN

PIG PROTEIN

CHICKEN PROTEIN

ROMANTIC LOVE

DEER PROTEIN

FISH
(SPORT ONLY!)

TORSO
Should be thick and impenetrable.

OLD WOODEN SAILING SHIPS
They're beautiful.

B.O.
Cultivating a manly musk puts your opponents on notice.

STILLNESS
Don't waste energy moving unless necessary.

SKIM MILK
Avoid it.

CURSING
There's only one bad word: Taxes. If any other word is good enough for sailors, it's good enough for you.

INTENSITY
Give 100%. 110% is impossible. Only idiots recommend that.

PROPERTY RIGHTS
They exist. Do not let them be taken away from you.

MASONRY
Building walls makes you strong. Defending them makes you even stronger.

CABINS
A place to rest that is made of logs.

PERSPIRATION
Only sweat during physical activity or love making. No emotional sweating.

YOU
You are your biggest ally.

CRYING
Acceptable at funerals and the Grand Canyon.

PHYSICAL FITNESS

FRIENDS
One to three is sufficient.

CAPITALISM
God's way of determining who is smart, and who is poor.

FACIAL HAIR
Full, thick and square. Nothing sculpted. If you have to sculpt it, that probably means you can't grow it.

LIVING IN THE WOODS
Live off the land.

RAGE
One rage every three months is permitted. Try not to hurt anyone who doesn't deserve it.

SECURITY
Secure the land.

POISE
Sting like a bee. Do not float like a butterfly. That's ridiculous.

HANDSHAKES
Firm, Dry, Solid. 3 seconds.

BODY GROOMING
Only women shave beneath the neck.

FRANKNESS
Cut the B.S.

SWANSON PYRAMID OF GREATNESS

Appendix 3:
Raccoon Safety Information

Things That Pawnee Raccoons Are Not Afraid Of

Daylight	Loud honking	Possums	Fences
Dogs, cats, or other pets	Animal control	Verbal threats	Guns
Humans	Garden hoses		

If you see a throng of raccoons (defined as twenty or more in one place), call **711**, which is the **Pawnee Municipal Raccoon Emergency Number**. If they have chewed your phone—which as of July 2008 seems more and more to be their M.O.—seek shelter in the nearest *concrete* structure and cover your head.

Most buildings in Pawnee also have **Red Light Emergency Phones** on the southern-facing wall. These are direct Raccoon Emergency Hotlines. *(Note: If you are being mugged, assailed, or robbed, please do not use the REH. We have too many legitimate raccoon emergencies and cannot afford to waste time dealing with human-on-human crimes.)*

Appendix 4:
Pawnee's 10 Worst Disasters

Great Pawnee Fire 1910
Pretty Impressive Pawnee Fire (née Great Pawnee Fire). 1899
Pawnee Bread Factory Fire (see sidebar below) 1922
Sweetums Nougat Flood (see sidebar below) 1919
Pawnee Downs Fire. 1911
Terrible Three-Year Fire of 1914–1917 1914–1917
Terrible Three-Year Fire of 1918–1921 1918–1921
Sweetums Nougat Riots 1920
Rather Humdrum Pawnee Fire (née Great Pawnee Fire). 1896
Central Firehouse Fire. 1903

Pawnee Bread Factory Fire

Fire broke out at the historic Pawnee Bread Factory on the morning of June 8, 1922. It is now believed that the fire was caused by some prohibited lunch-break toast making. However, at the time, local malcontent Arthur Dansbury-Witt was convicted of thirty-three counts of arson-related manslaughter and one count of a newly created crime called "attempted destruction of famous recipes." Since the latter crime came with the penalty of death, Dansbury-Witt was sentenced to immolation in the public square. Thousands gathered in Ramsett Park to cheer his burning. The cheering stopped, however, when the fire that was used to kill Dansbury-Witt spread to the newly rebuilt Pawnee Downs and burned it to the ground.

Sweetums Nougat Flood

On Sunday, May 2, 1919, Sweetums employees and their families gathered on the great lawn outside of the Sweetums factory for the company's annual Family Appreciation Day. The families spread out blankets and picnicked on the lawn while Sweetums management sat at banquet tables on a raised platform. Suddenly, one of the immense nougat silos ruptured, sending a wave of delicious, gooey, nutty, chocolatey, liquid death gushing toward the crowd. More than twenty people were killed, one hundred were injured, and one was inspired—a Sweetums engineer, who got the idea for their successful line of "Gushers," liquid nougat–filled candies.

People say that on hot summer days, the grass still smells of sugar. And the dead.

Appendix 5:
Nick Newport's Letter to His Children

This is the letter that Nick Newport, Sr., wrote to his family in order to get them to continue their horrible-but-profitable tabloid adventures.

August 30, 2004

Dear children, grandchildren, family ne'er-do-wells, etc.,

This is Nick Sr. Recently, as you all know, my son Calbert founded a trashy broadsheet whose aim it is to tear down this family. Ordinarily, this kind of treason would result in him being completely cut off from both my fortune and good graces forever. If you don't believe me, just ask Elizabeth's fourth son Gregory, who once tried to unionize my factory's workers. Oh wait, you cannot—he lives in a refrigerator crate next to an abandoned leather tannery, and was recently forced to trade his teeth for medicine.

However, in this case, Calbert's destructive actions have resulted in him falling ass-backwards into the first honest day's work he has ever had. Cal is now the editor of his own newspaper, the Pawnee Sun, a wretched value-less hodge-podge of altered photographs, half-truths, and betrayals that has proved to be quite profitable, thanks to the miserable, sniveling, spiritless, entertainment-starved street urchins that inhabit this pathetic village my grandfather had the grave misfortune of settling in a hundred-some years ago.

Those of you in close contact with my immediate family will note that Calbert's job is not only his first steady employment, it represents the very first paycheck any of my miserable offspring will have cashed that does not have my company's name in the watermark. Simply by holding a job, Calbert has now leapt to the front of the line of people who might possibly be able to run this company when I die. (Everyone else is tied for last.) And since the success of his weekly, contemptible gossip rag depends mostly on airing this family's dirty laundry, I hereby command all of you: change nothing.

Continue to live the selfish, purposeless, scandal-plagued lives you have been leading. Continue to spend my money thoughtlessly, cheat on your spouses, and blow powder up your surgically-altered noses.

Periodically, word will come to me that such-and-such grandchild is considering psychotherapy, or so-and-so niece feels ready for detox. If you are thinking about becoming better people, hold off just a little longer. For the sake of this family's future, please continue to do everything you can to tear this family apart.

Cordially,

Nick

NEN/cl
Dictated but not read

Appendix 6:
Additional Epigraphs

It took me like two hundred hours to decide which quotes should appear at the front of this book. The publisher was adamant that there be only three. I argued vehemently that instead of "three," which was boring, there should actually be 196—one for each year since Pawnee was founded. Words were exchanged, the most important of which was the publisher saying to me, "You have steamrolled me on every single issue I have ever brought up, and I have rolled over every single time, and I am drawing a line in the sand at having 196 damn epigraphs before you even start the book." I decided to let him have that one.

But it was very hard to choose only three of the quotes that have inspired me, and which I thought were relevant to this book and my view of the town and the world as a whole. So here are a bunch of others. (I won't include all 193 runners-up. Just some of my faves.)

In a country as big as the United States, you can find fifty examples of anything.
—JEFFERY F. CHAMBERLAIN

*Is the small town a place, truly, of the world, or is it no more than something
out of a boy's dreaming? Out of his love of all things not of death made? All things
somewhere beyond the dust, rust, and decay, beyond the top, beyond all sides,
beyond bottom: outside, around, over, under, within?*
—WILLIAM SAROYAN

Passion is energy. Feel the power that comes from focusing on what excites you.
—OPRAH

There are no common people, except in the highest spheres of society.
—MARK TWAIN

*What's right about America is that although we have a mess of problems, we have
great capacity—intellect and resources—to do something about them.*
—HENRY FORD II

A small town is a place where there's no place to go where you shouldn't.
—BURT BACHARACH

*An ardent supporter of the hometown team should go to a game
prepared to take offense, no matter what happens.*
—ROBERT BENCHLEY

To me, every hour of the day and night is an unspeakably perfect miracle.
—WALT WHITMAN

But for now we are young / Let us lay in the sun / And count every beautiful thing we can see.
—NEUTRAL MILK HOTEL

*Promise me you'll always remember: You're braver than you believe,
and stronger than you seem, and smarter than you think.*
—CHRISTOPHER ROBIN, TO WINNIE THE POOH

*I suppose one ought not to hire a magician, and then complain
that he does not behave like other people.*
—SUSANNA CLARKE

We are all imperfect. We cannot expect perfect government.
—WILLIAM HOWARD TAFT

*Now, as I am talking for Hartford, I will talk earnestly but modestly. There is much here to
see—the state house, Colt's factory and the place where the Charter Oak was. And we have
an antiquity here—the East Hartford bridge. Now let me beseech you, don't go away without
seeing that tunnel on stilts. You may think it a trifle, but go see it! Think what it may be to your
posterity, generations hence, who come here and say, "There's that same old bridge."*
—MARK TWAIN

Look. I'm not crazy.

I know Pawnee isn't Paris, or London, or Chicago, or even Indianapolis. I know there are prettier towns, and more vibrant cities, and more scenic drives, and better destinations. I know that to an outsider, it must seem like a waste of time for someone to spend her life defending a place that is, in some ways, indefensible. And it probably seems downright loony for that same person to spend six months slaving away, to conscript all of her friends and coworkers, and to write an entire book about that place, and all of its historical oddities.

I get that it maybe seems that way to you. And I don't care.

I was born here, I've lived here most of my life, and I love it. I love it to death. It's a great place to live, and work, and serving the goofballs in this town is an honor and a privilege, one I wouldn't trade for any other job. (Except for one where I got to serve them from Washington, D.C. I will take that job, happily, if you're offering.) Because in the words of one of the all-time greatest Pawneeans, Mr. Ron Swanson, when I asked him if I should accept an attractive offer to work in Eagleton: "You'll get a lot of job offers in your life, but you only have one hometown."

Yes, every place in America has a story to tell, and many of them I'm sure are fascinating. And yes, the world's great cities hold endless joys and adventures within their borders. And yes, every town claims its diner's waffles are the best in the world. But somewhere, in some town, there really *are* the best waffles in the world. Somewhere, there's a stack of waffles so delicious, and rich, and golden brown, and wonderful, that anyone who tasted them would decide never to leave that town. Somewhere, those waffles exist.

Why can't it be here?

Leslie Knope,
October 2011

Additional Acknowledgments

In addition to those already mentioned, many others contributed to this project in various important ways. In some sense, I guess you could say that these are the people who truly wrote the book. (Metaphorically. I wrote the book. Let's be clear.)

Nate DiMeo, from the Pawnee Historical Society, worked tirelessly and wonderfully to make sure this tome was as perfect as possible. And even though I was right about most of the historical stuff we argued about, and you were wrong, and that was proven each and every time we looked something up, I am still grateful for your help—even though your crazy dog chewed up my desk chair and you totally pretended not to notice and haven't yet offered to pay for it.

Janitors Frederick Armisen, Benjamin Schwartz, and Nicholas Offerman sneakily pilfered extra paper when I needed it, and let me into the building after hours, and for that I am eternally grateful, and I am also sorry that when they found out you guys got suspended without pay.

Local artist James Burke chipped in, when I needed some art for the section on Pawnee's raccoon problem. He drew those clip art–level raccoons with great skill and alacrity, and if any of you out there ever need drawings of raccoons, for whatever reason (signs warning people of local swarms, perhaps?), I highly recommend James. (By the way, James, if you're reading this, the $50 Food 'N Stuff gift certificate we promised you is on its way—I swear. Sorry it has taken five months to pay you.)

I would also like to thank Mrs. Turkleman's Fourth Grade Class, who recently toured the building on a field trip: Mikey Schurl, Normy Hiccox, Emmy Spivers, Danny Gorp, Emily Kenpak, Al Yang, Katie Dipples, Eeshmu Harrar, Harry Wittels, Chelsea P. Veretti, Ian Phipples, Phillip Davids, and adorable class president Ms. Morgan Sackett. Your pretty drawings of City Hall, and incoherent scribblings about what government means to you, are a true source of inspiration.

Leslie Knope
October 2011

A Brief Note on the Typeface

This book is printed in the font known as "Prairie Strong," designed by Jørgen Svensson in 1924. Svensson, who studied under Walter Gropius (founder of Berlin's famous Bauhaus design school), was asked to design a typeface for the *Pawnee Journal*. Svensson worked for months to devise Prairie Strong, saying that "its decisive, forthright lines embody the reserved yet dignified spirit of the people I have come to so admire since arriving here in the American Midwest." In its survey of American design in 1935, the New York Museum of Modern Art's famed curator Alfred Barr, Jr., wrote:

"Jørgen Svensson's 'Prairie Strong' is exactly the same as Times New Roman. Literally. He simply took Times New Roman—an extremely famous and popular font, mind you—and copied it, and claimed it was a new thing that he invented. It's preposterous. It's just exactly, 100% the same. And the fact that no one in that hick Indiana town seems to have figured this out confirms that they are all a bunch of moon-faced rubes."

To which I respond by writing "***Shove it, Alfred Barr, Jr.***" in Prairie Strong Condensed Bold Italic.